W9-BNS-325

elevate science

SAVVAS

LEARNING COMPANY

You're an author!

As you write in this science book, your answers and personal discoveries will be recorded for you to keep, making this book unique to you. That is why you are one of the primary authors of this book.

✎ In the space below, print your name, school, town, and state. Then write a short autobiography that includes your interests and accomplishments.

YOUR NAME ....

SCHOOL ....

TOWN, STATE ....

AUTOBIOGRAPHY ....

Your Photo

Cover: The cover shows a Joshua tree and a Joshua tree bloom in Joshua Tree National Park. Many interesting rock formations are also found in the park. In the sky a star factory of more than 800,000 stars is being born. FCVR: Casey Kiernan/Moment/Getty Images, Meganopierson/Shutterstock, Zoonar GmbH/Alamy Stock Photo, Stocktrek Images, Inc./Alamy Stock Photo; BCVR: Marinello/DigitalVision Vectors/Getty Images.

Attributions of third party content appear on page 138, which constitutes an extension of this copyright page.

"Next Generation Science Standards for California Public Schools, Kindergarten through Grade Twelve (CA NGSS)," by the California Department of Education. Copyright © California Department of Education. Used by permission.

Next Generation Science Standards is a registered trademark of WestEd. Neither WestEd nor the lead states and partners that developed the Next Generation Science Standards were involved in the production of this product, and do not endorse it. NGSS Lead States. 2013. Next Generation Science Standards: For States, By States. Washington, DC: The National Academies Press.

ISBN-13: 978-1-418-31039-4
ISBN-10:   1-418-31039-5
3 21

Program Authors

ZIPPORAH MILLER, Ed.D.

Coordinator for K-12 Science Programs, Anne Arundel County Public Schools

Dr. Zipporah Miller currently serves as the Senior Manager for Organizational Learning with the Anne Arundel County Public School System. Prior to that she served as the K-12 Coordinator for science in Anne Arundel County. She conducts national training to science stakeholders on the Next Generation Science Standards. Dr. Miller also served as the Associate Executive Director for Professional Development Programs and conferences at the National Science Teachers Association (NSTA) and served as a reviewer during the development of Next Generation Science Standards. Dr. Miller holds a doctoral degree from the University of Maryland College Park, a master's degree in school administration and supervision from Bowie State University and a bachelor's degree from Chadron State College.

MICHAEL J. PADILLA, Ph.D.

Professor Emeritus, Eugene P. Moore School of Education, Clemson University, Clemson, South Carolina

Michael J. Padilla taught science in middle and secondary schools, has more than 30 years of experience educating middle-school science teachers, and served as one of the writers of the 1996 U.S. National Science Education Standards. In recent years Mike has focused on teaching science to English Language Learners. His extensive experience as Principal Investigator on numerous National Science Foundation and U.S. Department of Education grants resulted in more than $35 million in funding to improve science education. He served as president of the National Science Teachers Association, the world's largest science teaching organization, in 2005–6.

MICHAEL E. WYSESSION, Ph.D

Professor of Earth and Planetary Sciences, Washington University, St. Louis, Missouri

Author of more than 100 science and science education publications, Dr. Wysession was awarded the prestigious National Science Foundation Presidential Faculty Fellowship and Packard Foundation Fellowship for his research in geophysics, primarily focused on using seismic tomography to determine the forces driving plate tectonics. Dr. Wysession is also a leader in geoscience literacy and education; he is the chair of the Earth Science Literacy Initiative, the author of several popular video lectures on geology in the *Great Courses* series, and a lead writer of the *Next Generation Science Standards**.

Program Consultants

Carol Baker
Science Curriculum

Dr. Carol K. Baker is superintendent for Lyons Elementary K-8 School District in Lyons, Illinois. Prior to this, she was Director of Curriculum for Science and Music in Oak Lawn, Illinois. Before this she taught Physics and Earth Science for 18 years. In the recent past, Dr. Baker also wrote assessment questions for ACT (EXPLORE and PLAN), was elected president of the Illinois Science Teachers Association from 2011–2013, and served as a member of the Museum of Science and Industry (Chicago) advisory board. She is a writer of the Next Generation Science Standards. Dr. Baker received her B.S. in Physics and a science teaching certification. She completed her master's of Educational Administration (K-12) and earned her doctorate in Educational Leadership.

Jim Cummins
ELL

Dr. Cummins's research focuses on literacy development in multilingual schools and the role technology plays in learning across the curriculum. *Elevate Science* incorporates research-based principles for integrating language with the teaching of academic content based on Dr. Cummins's work.

Elfrieda Hiebert
Literacy

Dr. Hiebert, a former primary-school teacher, is President and CEO of TextProject, a non-profit aimed at providing open-access resources for instruction of beginning and struggling readers, She is also a research associate at the University of California Santa Cruz. Her research addresses how fluency, vocabulary, and knowledge can be fostered through appropriate texts, and her contributions have been recognized through awards such as the Oscar Causey Award for Outstanding Contributions to Reading Research (Literacy Research Association, 2015), Research to Practice award (American Educational Research Association, 2013), and the William S. Gray Citation of Merit Award for Outstanding Contributions to Reading Research (International Reading Association, 2008).

Content Reviewers

Alex Blom, Ph.D.
Associate Professor
Department Of Physical Sciences
Alverno College
Milwaukee, Wisconsin

Joy Branlund, Ph.D.
Department of Physical Science
Southwestern Illinois College
Granite City, Illinois

Judy Calhoun
Associate Professor
Physical Sciences
Alverno College
Milwaukee, Wisconsin

Stefan Debbert
Associate Professor of Chemistry
Lawrence University
Appleton, Wisconsin

Diane Doser
Professor
Department of Geological Sciences
University of Texas at El Paso
El Paso, Texas

Rick Duhrkopf, Ph.D.
Department of Biology
Baylor University
Waco, Texas

Jennifer Liang
University of Minnesota Duluth
Duluth, Minnesota

Heather Mernitz, Ph.D.
Associate Professor of Physical
  Sciences
Alverno College
Milwaukee, Wisconsin

Joseph McCullough, Ph.D.
Cabrillo College
Aptos, California

Katie M. Nemeth, Ph.D.
Assistant Professor
College of Science and Engineering
University of Minnesota Duluth
Duluth, Minnesota

Maik Pertermann
Department of Geology
Western Wyoming Community College
Rock Springs, Wyoming

Scott Rochette
Department of the Earth Sciences
The College at Brockport
  State University of New York
Brockport, New York

David Schuster
Washington University in St Louis
St. Louis, Missouri

Shannon Stevenson
Department of Biology
University of Minnesota Duluth
Duluth, Minnesota

Paul Stoddard, Ph.D.
Department of Geology and
  Environmental Geosciences
Northern Illinois University
DeKalb, Illinois

Nancy Taylor
American Public University
Charles Town, West Virginia

Teacher Reviewers

Rita Armstrong
Los Cerritos Middle School
Thousand Oaks, California

Tyler C. Britt, Ed.S.
Curriculum & Instructional
Practice Coordinator
Raytown Quality Schools
Raytown, Missouri

Holly Bowser
Barstow High School
Barstow, California

David Budai
Coachella Valley Unified School District
Coachella, California

A. Colleen Campos
Grandview High School
Aurora, Colorado

Jodi DeRoos
Mojave River Academy
Colton, California

Colleen Duncan
Moore Middle School
Redlands, California

Nicole Hawke
Westside Elementary
Thermal, California

Margaret Henry
Lebanon Junior High School
Lebanon, Ohio

Ashley Humphrey
Riverside Preparatory Elementary
Oro Grande, California

Adrianne Kilzer
Riverside Preparatory Elementary
Oro Grande, California

Danielle King
Barstow Unified School District
Barstow, California

Kathryn Kooyman
Riverside Preparatory Elementary
Oro Grande, California

Esther Leonard M.Ed. and L.M.T.
Gifted and Talented Implementation Specialist
San Antonio Independent School District
San Antonio, Texas

Diana M. Maiorca, M.Ed.
Los Cerritos Middle School
Thousand Oaks, California

Kevin J. Maser, Ed.D.
H. Frank Carey Jr/Sr High School
Franklin Square, New York

Corey Mayle
Brogden Middle School
Durham, North Carolina

Keith McCarthy
George Washington Middle School
Wayne, New Jersey

Rudolph Patterson
Cobalt Institute of Math and Science
Victorville, California

Yolanda O. Peña
John F. Kennedy Junior High School
West Valley City, Utah

Stacey Phelps
Mojave River Academy
Oro Grande, California

Susan Pierce
Bryn Mawr Elementary
Redlands Unified School District
Redlands, California

Cristina Ramos
Mentone Elementary School
Redlands Unified School District
Mentone, California

Mary Regis
Franklin Elementary School
Redlands, California

Bryna Selig
Gaithersburg Middle School
Gaithersburg, Maryland

Pat (Patricia) Shane, Ph.D.
STEM & ELA Education Consultant
Chapel Hill, North Carolina

Elena Valencia
Coral Mountain Academy
Coachella, California

Janelle Vecchio
Mission Elementary School
Redlands, California

Brittney Wells
Riverside Preparatory Elementary
Oro Grande, California

Kristina Williams
Sequoia Middle School
Newbury Park, California

Safety Reviewers

Douglas Mandt, M.S.
Science Education Consultant
Edgewood, Washington

Juliana Textley, Ph.D.
Author, NSTA books on school science safety
Adjunct Professor
Lesley University
Cambridge, Massachusetts

California Spotlight
Instructional Segment 2

TOPICS 3–5

Ocean Acidification

TOPIC 3 Chemical Reactions 8

Investigative Phenomenon How can analyzing and interpreting data help you determine when a chemical reaction has occurred?

MS-PS1-2, MS-PS1-3, MS-PS1-5, MS-PS1-6, EP&CIa, EP&CIIb

HANDS-ON LABS

Connect
Investigate
Demonstrate

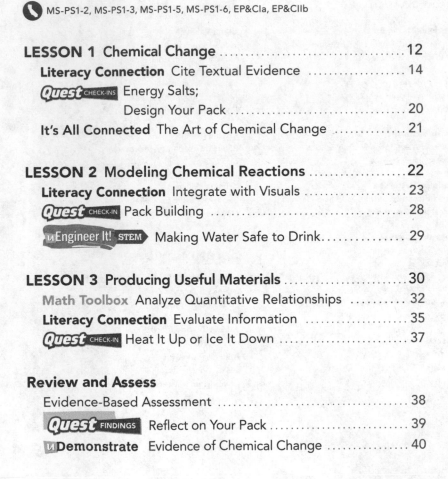

🕐 MS-LS1-6, MS-LS1-7, EP&CIIIa, EP&CIIIb

HANDS-ON LABS

иConnect

иInvestigate

иDemonstrate

HANDS-ON LABS

и**Connect**
и**Investigate**
и**Demonstrate**

Go to SavvasRealize.com to access your digital course.

Elevate Science combines the best science narrative with a robust online program. Throughout the lessons, digital support is presented at point of use to enhance your learning experience.

Online Resources

Savvas Realize™ is your online science class. This digital-learning environment includes:

- Student eTEXT
- Instructor eTEXT
- Project-Based Learning
- Virtual Labs
- Interactivities
- Videos
- Assessments
- Study Tools
- and more!

Digital Features

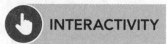 VIDEO

Keep an eye out for these **icons**, which indicate the different ways your textbook is enhanced online.

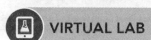 INTERACTIVITY

 VIRTUAL LAB

Digital activities are located throughout the narrative to deepen your understanding of scientific concepts.

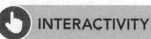 INTERACTIVITY

Interpret models of relationships in various ecosystems.

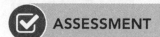 ASSESSMENT

 eTEXT

APP

Elevate your thinking!

California Elevate Science takes science to a whole new level and lets you take ownership of your learning. Explore science in the world around you. Investigate how things work. Think critically and solve problems! *California Elevate Science* helps you think like a scientist, so you're ready for a world of discoveries.

Exploring California

California spotlights explore California phenomena. Topic Quests help connect lesson concepts together and reflect 3-dimensional learning.

- Science concepts organized around phenomena
- Topics weave together 3-D learning
- Engineering focused on solving problems and improving designs

California Spotlight
Instructional Segment 2

Before the Topics
Identify the Problem

California Flood Management

Phenomenon In February of 2017, workers at the Oroville Dam were forced to use the

Student Discourse

California Elevate Science promotes active discussion, higher order thinking and analysis and prepares you for high school through:

- High-level write-in prompts
- Evidence-based arguments
- Practice in speaking and writing

Model It

Crystalline and Amorphous Solids
Figure 5 A pat of butter is an amorphous solid. The particles that make up the butter are not arranged in a regular pattern. The sapphire gem stones are crystalline solids. Draw what you think the particles look like in a crystalline solid.

☑ **READING CHECK** Explain
In your own words, explain the main differences between crystalline solids and amorphous solids.

Quest CHECK-IN

In this lesson, you learned what happens to the particles of substances during melting, freezing, evaporation, boiling, condensation, and sublimation. You also thought about how thermal energy plays a role in these changes of state.

Predict Why do you need to take the temperature of the surroundings into consideration when designing a system with materials that can change state?

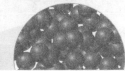

Academic Vocabulary

In orange juice, bits of pulp are suspended in liquid. Explain what you think *suspended* means.

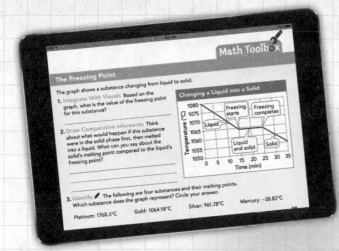

The Freezing Point

The graph shows a substance changing from liquid to solid.

1. Integrate With Visuals Based on the graph, what is the value of the freezing point for this substance?

2. Draw Comparative Inferences Think about what would happen if this substance were in the solid phase first, then melted into a liquid. What can you say about the solid's melting point compared to the liquid's freezing point?

3. Identify The following are four substances and their melting points. Which substance does the graph represent? Circle your answer.

Platinum: 1768.3°C   Gold: 1064.18°C   Silver: 961.78°C   Mercury: −38.83°C

Changing a Liquid into a Solid

Math Toolbox

Build Literacy Skills

By connecting science to other disciplines like:

- Mathematics
- Reading and Writing
- STEM/Engineering

Focus on Inquiry

Case studies put you in the shoes of a scientist to solve real-world mysteries using real data. You will be able to:

- Analyze data
- Formulate claims
- Build evidence-based arguments

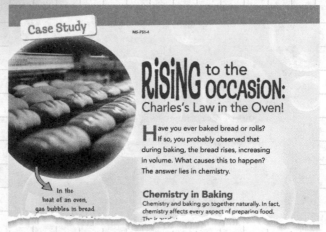

Case Study   MS-PS1-4

RiSiNG to the OCCASION: Charles's Law in the Oven!

In the heat of an oven, gas bubbles in bread

Have you ever baked bread or rolls? If so, you probably observed that during baking, the bread rises, increasing in volume. What causes this to happen? The answer lies in chemistry.

Chemistry in Baking

Chemistry and baking go together naturally. In fact, chemistry affects every aspect of preparing food.

Enter the Digital Classroom

Virtual labs, 3-D expeditions, and dynamic videos take science beyond the classroom.

- Open-ended virtual labs
- Google Expeditions and field trips
- NBC Learn videos

Alike and Different: Living Things

Click the pictures. Compare how living things and their parents are alike and different. Write your answer below.

Type your answer here.

NBC LEARN VIDEO

After watching the Quest Kickoff video about how coastal engineers study and reduce coastal erosion, complete the 3-2-1 activity.

How do changes in the atmosphere and ocean affect living and nonliving things?

Explore It

Look at the picture. What do you observe? What questions do you have about the phenomenon? Write your observations and questions in the space below.

....

....

....

....

....

....

....

....

....

....

....

....

....

....

....

....

....

....

....

....

....

....

....

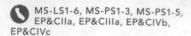
MS-LS1-6, MS-PS1-3, MS-PS1-5,
EP&CIIa, EP&CIIIa, EP&CIVb,
EP&CIVc

Inquiry

- How do rocks and minerals reflect the cycling of matter?
- How do human-caused changes in the atmosphere affect chemical reactions in the ocean?
- How do changes in atmosphere and ocean chemistry affect organisms' ability to perform basic functions?

Topics

Before the Topics
Identify the Problem

Ocean Acidification

Phenomenon Channel Islands National Park consists of five rugged islands along the coast of southern California. The islands are carefully managed to prevent damage from human activities. However, the islands are impacted by changes in the chemistry of our planet's atmosphere and ocean. These changes are causing ocean water to become more acidic, which threatens the survival of many species.

Even though they are remote and wild, the Channel Islands do not have a pristine environment. They are all impacted by human activities.

The Channel Islands

The eight Channel Islands formed millions of years ago from complex geological processes. These processes continue to influence the height, size, and position of each island.

Channel Island National Park is a living laboratory, where scientists can learn about natural systems and how they change over time. Little human activity is allowed on the islands. The waters around each island are protected from fishing and most recreation. As a result, natural processes continue undisturbed. The table shows some of the factors that affect the national park islands.

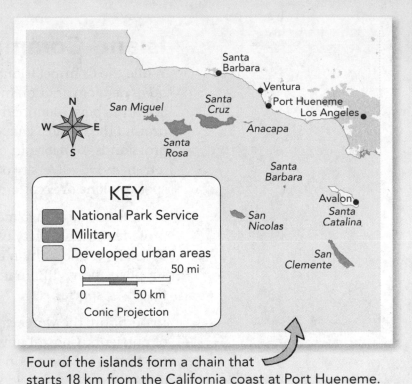

Four of the islands form a chain that starts 18 km from the California coast at Port Hueneme.

Event	Caused by Humans or Nature?
The Pacific plate rises, pushing the Channel Islands above the water surface.	NATURE
Water levels fell during the last ice age until the four northern islands were all connected above sea level.	NATURE
Native American Chumash and Tongva peoples lived on the islands and harvested shellfish.	HUMANS
Wind and water wear down the rocks of the islands.	BOTH
Mammoths and other land animals swam across to the islands from the mainland.	BOTH
Sea level is rising as the global temperature increases.	HUMANS
The skeletons of living things built up over time to make fossil beds near the shore.	HUMANS
Carbon dioxide in the air increases and dissolves into ocean water, making it more acidic.	HUMANS

CCC Cause and Effect 🖊 Both past and current natural events, as well as human activities, affect the Channel Islands. Complete the table by identifying whether each event is caused by humans or nature.

3

Island Communities

While the Channel Islands only cover a small area, there is a great deal of variation in their physical features and conditions. Scientists have identified seven main types of ecosystems on and around the islands: chaparral, oak woodlands, scrub, marsh, grasslands, kelp forests, and eelgrass beds. The islands contain a tremendous diversity of living things. Eight hundred plant species alone are scattered throughout these ecosystems.

The islands also have many different physical features that provide a wide variety of habitats. Separate populations thrive at sea level and at high elevations. Flat land with good soil supports many different species. Steep, rocky land supports far fewer species.

In addition, the water around the islands contains high levels of nutrients. Coastal upwelling carries nutrient-rich water from the bottom of the ocean up to the surface near the islands. Kelp forests grow in this cold water, which provide shelter and food for many different species. Kelp and other green organisms take in sunlight and carbon dioxide and use them to grow.

The Channel Islands host an array of different living communities.

Scrub is one of many habitats on Santa Cruz Island.

Island chaparral supports an array of wildlife.

Eelgrass provides shelter for fish, shellfish, and tiny organisms.

The Ocean Food Web

Plankton are tiny organisms in the ocean, and they can be divided into two categories. Phytoplankton are plant-like organisms that consume carbon dioxide and produce oxygen through photosynthesis. These organisms produce half the world's supply of oxygen. Zooplankton are animals or animal-like organisms that eat the phytoplankton or other zooplankton. They need oxygen to live, and they also produce carbon dioxide.

The waters off the coast of the Channel Islands support plankton of all kinds. The shallow water provides the sunlight and nutrients that plankton need. Kelp and seagrass beds provide shelter from waves and predators. Many larger species, from fish to blue whales, depend on plankton for food, making plankton the base of the ocean food web.

Plankton are quite sensitive to changes in ocean temperature and chemistry. Scientists are already finding that phytoplankton populations have decreased in many places around the world. This fact could spell trouble if global warming continues.

Thousands of animal species live among the kelp.

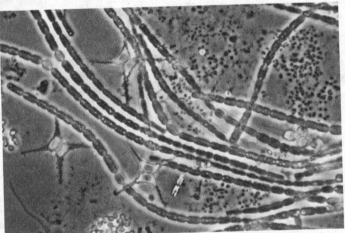

Phytoplankton produce their own food, forming the base of the ocean food web.

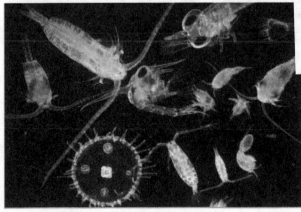

Many species of zooplankton drift together in the ocean.

CCC Apply Concepts Identify at least three organisms that need oxygen to survive and three organisms that consume carbon dioxide to survive.

fish, humans, and horses consume O2. kelp, trees, and veggies need CO2

Carbon and Ocean Acidification

For hundreds of millions of years, marine organisms lived, died, and sank to the bottom of the sea. Over time, their bodies fossilized and turned into oil, coal, and natural gas. The carbon dioxide consumed by the organisms is trapped in these fossil fuels.

Today, humans burn fossil fuels for energy. Burning returns carbon dioxide to the atmosphere. Increasing levels of carbon dioxide in the atmosphere contribute to global warming. Carbon dioxide in the atmosphere also dissolves into ocean water. It reacts with water to produce a compound called carbonic acid. Scientists have observed that the acidity of ocean water has been increasing due to the burning of fossil fuels.

In 2014, Dr. Nina Bednarsek and her team from the National Oceanic and Atmospheric Administration (NOAA) reported evidence that ocean acidification is harming zooplankton:

> [Fifty-three] percent of pteropods sampled using a fine mesh net had severely dissolved shells. The ocean's absorption of human-caused carbon dioxide emissions is also increasing the level of corrosive waters near the ocean's surface where pteropods live.

As you read the topics in this segment, think about how chemical reactions, cell processes, and minerals and rocks all contribute to scientists' understanding of ocean acidification and the Channel Islands system.

Pteropods are zooplankton related to snails. Found throughout the world's oceans, pteropods are a major food source for fish and whales. The images to the right show Dr. Bednarsek's evidence for damage to pteropods' calcium carbonate shells from acidic water.

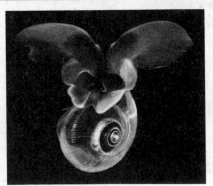

Pteropod, also known as Sea Butterfly

1. **SEP Analyze Data** How is the healthy pteropod shell different than the damaged shell?

   the healthy one is smooth.

2. **Predict** Look at the photo of the live, swimming pteropod. How might damage to its shell affect its survival?

   if the shell breaks, its innards would come out and it would die.

What questions can you ask to help you make sense of this phenomena?

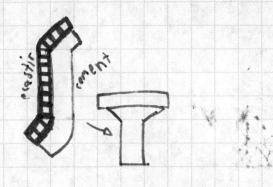

plastic

cement

Chemical Reactions

Investigative Phenomenon
How can analyzing and interpreting data help you determine when a chemical reaction has occurred?

MS-PS1-2 Analyze and interpret data on the properties of substances before and after the substances interact to determine if a chemical reaction has occurred.

MS-PS1-3 Gather and make sense of information to describe that synthetic materials come from natural resources and impact society.

MS-PS1-5 Develop and use a model to describe how the total number of atoms does not change in a chemical reaction and thus mass is conserved.

MS-PS1-6 Undertake a design project to construct, test, and modify a device that either releases or absorbs thermal energy by chemical processes.

EP&CIa Students should be developing an understanding that the goods produced by natural systems are essential to human life and to the functioning of our economies and cultures.

EP&CIIb Students should be developing an understanding that methods used to extract, harvest, transport, and consume natural resources influence the geographic extent, composition, biological diversity, and viability of natural systems.

What kinds of chemical changes occur in this aquarium?

Connect Explore what happens when chemicals react.

What questions do you have about the phenomenon?

....

....

....

....

....

....

....

....

....

....

....

Quest PBL

How can you design and build hot packs and cold packs?

STEM **Figure It Out** Every day, people test the strength, flexibility, and endurance of their bodies. They may be athletes, workers, or simply active children and adults. When minor injuries occur, applying heat or cold can ease pain, reduce swelling, and help damaged tissue begin to heal. Chemists and product engineers have designed easy-to-use packs that get hot or cold because of chemical reactions that users can activate when they need to. In this problem-based Quest activity, you will design and build a hot or cold pack for the treatment of minor injuries. You will determine which chemicals and materials best meet the criteria and constraints. After exploration, design, and testing, you will reflect on your product and its effectiveness.

After watching the Quest Kickoff video, in which a chemist describes chemical processes that release or absorb heat, think of other uses for a product that heats up or cools down. Record three ideas in the space provided.

1

....
....

2

....
....

3

....
....

👆 **INTERACTIVITY**

Hot and Cool Chemistry

🕓 MS-PS1-6, MS-ETS1-1, MS-ETS1-2, MS-ETS1-3, MS-ETS1-4

Quest CHECK-IN

IN LESSON 1

How do salts react with water? Explore whether various chemical interactions release or absorb (store) energy.

HANDS-ON LAB

Energy Salts

Quest CHECK-IN

IN LESSON 1

STEM Which chemical reaction will achieve the desired results in a hot or cold pack? Devise a plan for your chosen chemical reaction, including a design plan for the pack itself.

👆 **INTERACTIVITY**

Design Your Pack

Quest CHECK-IN

IN LESSON 2

STEM How can you construct your hot or cold pack? Choose materials, build a prototype using ordinary salt or sugar, and test your product.

HANDS-ON LAB

Pack Building

Instant cold packs don't need to be kept in a freezer or cooler, so they are easier to transport than ice. They can be activated the moment an injury occurs.

Quest CHECK-IN

IN LESSON 3

STEM How can you modify your design to construct a better prototype? Build an improved prototype using chemical salts and demonstrate the use of the product.

HANDS-ON LAB

Heat It Up or Ice It Down

Quest FINDINGS

Complete the Quest!

Based on results and feedback from your demonstration, evaluate the effectiveness of your hot or cold pack in producing a controlled flow of energy. Reflect on your work.

👆 **INTERACTIVITY**

Reflect on Your Pack

1 Chemical Change

uInvestigate Explore the chemical changes of a burning candle.

 MS-PS1-2 Analyze and interpret data on the properties of substances before and after the substances interact to determine if a chemical reaction has occurred.

Connect It !

✏️ **Complete the label on the image by identifying whether the raisins drying in the sun are an example of a physical or a chemical change.**

Make Observations What are some of the differences you can observe between a grape and a raisin?

....

....

....

Changing Matter

About 350,000 tons of raisins are produced each year in the United States. Most of these raisins are grown in the San Joaquin Valley, which is known as the raisin capital of the world (**Figure 1**). The entire process of growing grapes and producing raisins involves physical and chemical changes to matter.

HANDS-ON LAB

See if you can identify whether a substance has changed into another substance.

Physical Change A grape drying out in the sun is an example of a **physical change**—a change that alters the form or appearance of a substance without changing it into a different substance. The grape becomes smaller and wrinkled when the water in it evaporates, but the raisin produced is still made of the same matter as before. Water evaporating or boiling is also a physical change. While the water may not be visible as vapor in the air, it is still water. Bending, crushing, cutting, melting, freezing, and boiling are all physical changes.

While physical changes may alter some physical properties of an object, the characteristic physical properties of the matter remain the same. You can use those properties to identify a quantity of a substance. Some characteristic physical properties include density, conductivity, malleability, melting point, freezing point, and boiling point. For instance, the boiling point of water is 100°C. One drop of water and one liter will both boil at this temperature.

Physical and Chemical Changes
Figure 1 As these grapes on the vine sit in the sun, they dry into raisins.

Raisins drying in the sun are an example of a (physical / chemical) change.

13

Literacy Connection

Cite Textual Evidence
What is the difference between a physical change and a chemical change? Cite an example from the text that helps you understand this difference. Give a detailed description.

....

....

....

....

....

....

....

Chemical Change

Grapevines, like all plants, grow as the result of chemical reactions that form new compounds inside their cells. A chemical reaction can also be called a **chemical change**—a change in matter that produces one or more new substances. In a chemical change, atoms and molecules rearrange to form new combinations. Substances that undergo chemical changes are called **reactants**, and what they form are called **products**.

Burning and rusting are both examples of chemical changes. During these changes, characteristic chemical properties can be used to identify a quantity of a substance that is reacting. Flammability is the ability of a substance to burn and cause fire. When a substance burns, you can observe the substance's flammability. When iron rusts, you can observe its reactivity with oxygen. During both of these chemical reactions, changes in color provide evidence that a chemical reaction has occurred. Under given conditions, these chemical properties can be used to identify a quantity of a substance.

✓ CHECK POINT **Apply Concepts** A student uses flour, sugar, eggs, and butter to bake a cake. Is this an example of a chemical or physical change? Explain.

....

....

....

....

Model It

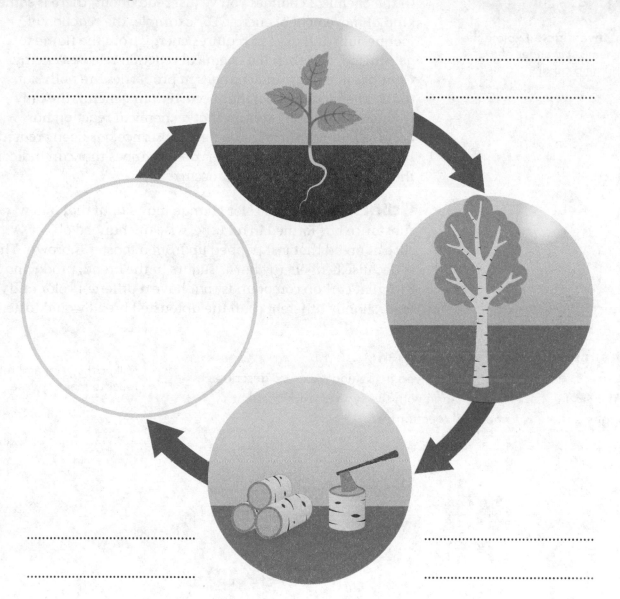

....
....

....

....

Wood Work

Figure 2 Cutting down a tree and burning the wood are parts of a cycle that involves many physical and chemical changes. After a seed sprouts, the seedling uses energy from the sun to turn carbon dioxide and water from its surroundings into food and oxygen. The seedling uses this food to grow into a tree. Then, when the wood is burned, some of the carbon dioxide in the smoke may end up being used by other trees to make food to grow!

SEP Develop Models ✏ Complete the model by drawing the last step of the cycle in the empty circle. Identify whether each part of the cycle involves a physical and/or chemical change.

Evidence of Chemical Reactions

In the chemical changes you've just read about, there is some kind of movement of energy. For example, the reaction of magnesium and oxygen requires energy from the flame to get started, and then the chemical reaction releases energy. Changes in energy and changes in properties are both signs that a chemical reaction has occurred. In general, the only way to be absolutely certain that a chemical reaction has occurred is to confirm that a new substance has been created. However, there are other observable changes that can indicate that a chemical reaction has occurred.

Color Change A color change may signal that a new substance has formed in an otherwise unchanged object. A slice of bread that just popped up from a toaster is brown. This is because heat energy burns sugars in the bread, producing different carbon compounds that have a different color and taste slightly different than the untoasted bread would taste.

Chemistry in the Pizza Kitchen

Figure 3 🖉 Three changes involved in making pizza are described in this figure. Label each change with the type of evidence that suggests there is a chemical reaction.

Milk, citric acid, and rennet react to make cheese.

....

....

Yeast cells consume sugars that are in flour. In the process, the yeast produces alcohol and carbon dioxide gas.

....

Gas Production Another observable change that is evidence of a chemical reaction is the production of gas from solid or liquid reactants. For example, the chemical reaction between vinegar and baking soda produces carbon dioxide gas. However, the presence of bubbles is not always a sign of a reaction taking place. Bubbles of carbon dioxide appear in soda when the bottle is opened and pressure is released. The only way to be certain that any chemical reaction has taken place is the presence of one or more new substances.

Formation of a Precipitate Mixing two liquids may produce a precipitate, which is a solid that forms from liquids. When milk and lemon juice are mixed, a chunky precipitate forms. Some dairy products are made by taking advantage of similar reactions between milk and other substances.

✓ CHECK POINT **Cite Textual Evidence** What is the only way to be certain that a chemical reaction has occurred?

....

....

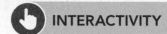

INTERACTIVITY

Watch a video of reactions and decide whether new substances have formed.

📓 **Write About It** What other physical or chemical changes might take place while making pizza? Write about them in your science notebook, noting whether each one is a physical or chemical change.

The cheese and pizza dough turn brown in some places when the pizza cooks.

....

....

Changes in Energy

You have seen that some chemical reactions, such as the browning that occurs on the surface of a pizza as it cooks, require energy in the form of heat. Other chemical reactions give off energy. Reactions are classified as absorbing or releasing energy, based on the direction of heat flow.

Reactions that Release Energy

In reactions that release energy, the energy is released as the products form. The energy is usually released as heat, or thermal energy. For example, some ovens and stoves burn natural gas. When natural gas burns, it releases heat. This heat cooks your food. Similarly, the reactions between oxygen and other flammable fuels, such as wood, coal or wax, release energy in the form of light and heat.

Reactions that Absorb Energy

In reactions that absorb energy, more energy is required to break down the reactants than is released by the formation of the products. Some reactions that absorb energy draw energy from their surroundings, leaving the surroundings feeling cold. Others require a continuous source of energy, like frying an egg in a pan on a stove.

☑ CHECK POINT **Infer** Does a hand-warming product that is worn inside gloves undergo a chemical reaction that absorbs or releases thermal energy? Explain your answer.

....

....

....

....

....

The Movement of Energy

Figure 4 The reaction of baking soda and vinegar absorbs energy from its surroundings. Kerosene in a lantern is burned to release energy. ✎ On each image, draw an arrow to indicate the direction in which energy moves as a result of the reaction that is occurring.

Movement of Thermal Energy In chemical reactions, thermal energy can be absorbed from or released into the surroundings of the reaction. When thermal energy is released, energy moves from the chemicals in the reaction to the surroundings. When thermal energy is absorbed, energy moves from the surroundings into the chemicals in the reaction. In **Figure 4**, oxygen reacts with kerosene oil in a lamp to release thermal energy into the surroundings. If you were to stand close enough to the lamp, you could feel the heat being released by the chemicals in the reaction. When baking soda and vinegar react (**Figure 4**), the chemicals in the reaction absorb thermal energy from the surrounding environment. If you were to touch the beaker after the chemical reaction has taken place, you would notice it feels colder.

☑ CHECK POINT **Apply Concepts** Instant cold packs contain water and a chemical called ammonium nitrate. When combined, the ammonium nitrate and water react to create a cold feeling. Is thermal energy absorbed or released during this chemical reaction? Explain.

....

....

....

....

MS-PS1-2

1. SEP Analyze Data While hiking in the woods, you see a brown, rotting apple lying on the ground. What changes in the physical properties of the apple are signs that a chemical reaction has occurred?

....

....

....

....

....

2. SEP Construct Explanations Explain how a substance's flammability can indicate a chemical change.

....

....

....

....

3. CCC Cause and Effect A clear liquid is poured into a beaker containing another clear liquid. A cloudy yellow substance forms, as if out of nowhere, but the rest of the liquid remains clear. What happened?

....

....

....

....

4. SEP Ask Questions Some silver coins are found inside an ancient shipwreck. They are coated with a black crust. Ask a question that could help you to determine whether the silver underwent a chemical change or a physical change. Explain.

....

....

....

....

Quest CHECK-IN

In this lesson, you learned how to distinguish physical changes from chemical changes. You also discovered how specific chemical changes can be observed and even controlled by paying attention to energy and other evidence.

Apply Scientific Reasoning What are some general rules or patterns you learned about in this lesson that you can apply when designing a device that will release or absorb a controlled amount of heat?

....

....

....

....

....

HANDS-ON LAB

Energy Salts

👆 INTERACTIVITY

Design Your Pack

Go online to download this lab worksheet. Test different salts to determine whether they meet a specific design criterion for use in an instant hot pack or cold pack—the release or absorption of energy.

Go online to brainstorm activation methods for your pack. Think about what materials you will use, and come up with your design plan. Make sure you know what experimental evidence to collect to show that your idea is workable.

The Art of
Chemical Change

Many artists paint landscapes or portraits. Others create multimedia works with sound and light. But some artists rely on chemical reactions to make their art. Acid etching is a process that some artists use to create beautiful artwork and jewelry, with metal as the canvas. Acid is used to etch designs into metals such as zinc, copper, brass, and even steel. When an acid reacts with a metal, it usually produces a salt and hydrogen gas. The metal loses atoms in the process. Hydrochloric acid, ferric nitrate, and sulfuric acid are some of the highly corrosive compounds used to produce this reactive art.

Film photographers also use chemical reactions when they process photographs. In photo processing, chemicals used to develop the photographs react with silver halides to create the darker areas of the image. Other artists use chemical reactions to create textiles, sculptures, and even movies.

CONNECT TO YOU

You've been asked to create a work of art that demonstrates the beauty of chemical reactions. What kind of artwork would you create? What kinds of chemical reactions would you incorporate into your art?

A photograph is processed in a darkened room, where a chemical reaction takes place on the photo paper.

Acid etching produced the patterns on this helmet. Helmets like this one might have been worn by the Spaniards who explored what is now California in the early 1500s.

21

Modeling Chemical Reactions

Connect It!

🖊 **The rust on this ship formed through a chemical reaction between iron and oxygen. Label the reactants and products in the equation.**

Identify What are the sources of the iron and oxygen that form the rust on this ship?

....

....

Chemical Equations

When you communicate with friends using digital devices, you probably use symbols, abbreviations, and other ways to shorten your messages. This makes communication more efficient. Instead of typing "just kidding," you may type two letters—"jk"—to convey the same information. Science—and chemistry in particular—also makes use of shorthand language to convey information. A chemical equation is a way to describe a chemical reaction using symbols instead of words.

Chemical equations are shorter than sentences, but they contain all of the necessary pieces of information to summarize a chemical reaction. Just as a cell phone user who reads "jk" needs to learn what that stands for, a scientist needs to learn how to read and write chemical equations. A chemical equation is a model of the unobservable mechanism of a reaction. The chemical equation that summarizes the reaction that makes rust is shown in the caption for **Figure 1**. The chemical equation conveys three things: the identities of the molecules involved in the reaction, the elements that make up those molecules, and whether the molecules are products or reactants.

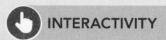

INTERACTIVITY

Write about the reaction that occurs when wood burns.

Literacy Connection

Integrate with Visuals
Set up a two-column table in your notebook. As you read through this lesson, record examples of chemical reactions. In one column, write a description of the reaction. In the other column, write its chemical equation.

Rusting Wreck
Figure 1 The process that transformed this ship's hull is a chemical reaction. Oxygen combines with iron to make iron oxide, which is commonly known as rust.

$$4\,Fe + 3\,O_2 \rightarrow 2\,Fe_2O_3$$

Formulas

A chemical formula combines the symbols of different elements to represent molecules. For example, the formula for water is H_2O. H is the symbol for hydrogen, and O is the symbol for oxygen. The subscript number next to a letter shows how many atoms of that element are in the molecule. There are two hydrogen atoms in water. If there is no subscript, it means there is only one atom of that element. There is only one atom of oxygen in water.

Structure of an Equation

All chemical equations share a basic structure. A chemical equation indicates the substances involved in a reaction and the substances that are formed as a result of the reaction. It can be shown as a flow diagram. The formulas for the reactants are on the left, followed by an arrow. The arrow means "yields," or "reacts to form." The formulas for the products are written to the right of the arrow. If there are two or more reactants, they are separated by a plus sign (+). If two or more products form, they are also separated by a plus sign.

Reactant + Reactant ⟶ Product + Product

The numbers in front of the components in the equation show how many particles of the reactants are needed and how many particles of the products are formed. These numbers, called *coefficients*, balance the equation so that the number of atoms in the reactants equals the number of atoms in the products.

Model It

Formation of Ammonia

Figure 2 The diagram of the molecules and the chemical equation are both models that represent the formation of ammonia from nitrogen and hydrogen gas.

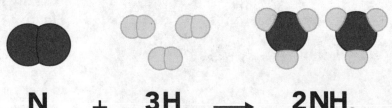

$$N_2 \ + \ 3H_2 \ \longrightarrow \ 2NH_3$$

1. **Claim** ✎ Circle the product and underline the coefficients in the chemical equation.

2. **Evidence** How many atoms of hydrogen are in one molecule of ammonia?

....

3. **Reasoning** Are any atoms created or destroyed in this reaction? Explain.

....

....

....

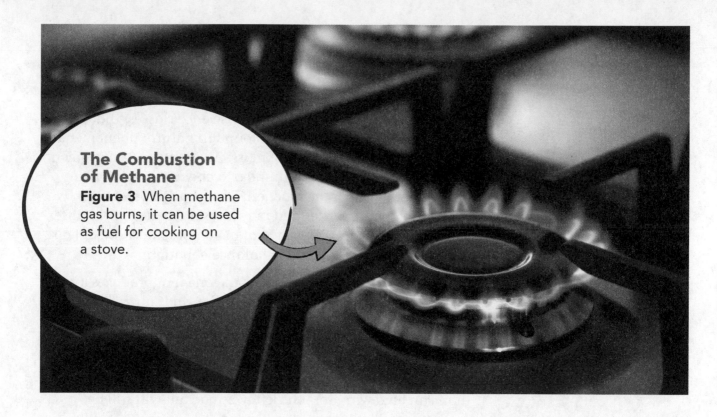

The Combustion of Methane

Figure 3 When methane gas burns, it can be used as fuel for cooking on a stove.

Chemical Reactions and Equations

The number of reactants and products can vary. Some reactions have only one reactant or product. Other reactions have two, three, or more reactants or products. For example, the reaction that occurs when limestone, or calcium carbonate ($CaCO_3$), is heated has one reactant and two products (CaO and CO_2).

$$CaCO_3 \longrightarrow CaO + CO_2$$

The reaction that occurs when methane gas (CH_4) is burned in the presence of oxygen features two reactants and two products.

$$CH_4 + 2O_2 \longrightarrow CO_2 + 2H_2O$$

Note that the flame that provides the energy for the reaction as shown in **Figure 3** is not itself a reactant. Only the substances that are chemically rearranged in the reaction are shown in the equation.

✓ CHECK POINT **Identify** Record the names and formulas of the reactants and products of methane combustion.

....

....

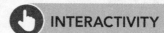

INTERACTIVITY

Use models to help you understand chemical reactions.

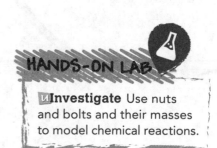

HANDS-ON LAB

и**Investigate** Use nuts and bolts and their masses to model chemical reactions.

Law of Conservation of Mass

When reactants form new products, the new products always have the same amount of matter as the reactants. During a chemical reaction, matter is neither created nor destroyed. Like other laws you have studied in your science classes, that principle is a statement of a pattern found in natural phenomena. It is the law of conservation of mass. All atoms of each element that are present at the beginning of a chemical reaction are present at the end of the reaction. Even though products may have different properties and may look and behave very differently from the reactants, the total mass does not change. This is why coefficients are used to balance equations.

For example, in a reaction such as the one that produces iron sulfide, the sum of the masses of iron (Fe) and sulfur (S) equals the mass of the iron sulfide (FeS) they produce (**Figure 4**). An atom of iron bonds with an atom of sulfur, and the masses of the individual atoms combine when they form molecules. If there is more iron than can bind with sulfur, or more sulfur than can bind with iron, the leftover reactant will still be present, as will its mass.

$$Fe + S \longrightarrow FeS$$

Mass Conserved

Figure 4 Iron and sulfur react to form iron sulfide. The masses of the reactants and the products are shown on the first set of scales. The second set of scales shows the masses of two liquid reactants. Fill in the expected mass of the liquid product for this second reaction.

✓ CHECK POINT **Integrate with Visuals** Explain how the masses on the scales in **Figure 4** demonstrate the law of conservation of mass.

....

....

Open Systems

Some reactions may appear to violate the principle of conservation of mass. Recall that photosynthesis is a chemical reaction that plants use to make food. Carbon dioxide from the air and water absorbed from soil are reactants that produce sugar and oxygen, thanks to the energy provided by sunlight. But if you measure the mass of a plant as it grows, it will seem that a huge amount of mass is appearing out of nowhere. This is because most plants we see are in an **open system**, where matter can enter and escape. The flow and invisibility of the carbon dioxide gas that plants convert to food and structures—stems, trunks, leaves, and so on—makes it very difficult to know just how much carbon dioxide is involved (**Figure 5**).

Closed Systems

A **closed system** is a better place in which to measure the movement of matter and study reactions that involve gas. The sealed system in **Figure 5** allows scientists to manipulate and analyze the contents of the system, including plants, without worrying that invisible gases may be moving into or out of the system.

VIDEO

Watch a video to gain a better understanding of conservation of mass.

INTERACTIVITY

Demonstrate how matter is conserved in the formation of water and the burning of methane.

Open and Closed Systems

Figure 5 System A shows an example of an open system, while System B shows an example of a closed system. In both cases, the properties of the reactants and products are different, but mass is conserved in all the reactions.

☑ LESSON 2 Check

1. **Identify** Aluminum (Al) and silver tarnish (Ag_2S) yield pure silver (Ag) in an aluminum sulfide solution.

$$3Ag_2S + 2Al \longrightarrow 6Ag + Al_2S_3$$

What are the reactants and products in this reaction?

....

....

....

....

2. **Infer** When wood burns in a campfire, the wood combines with oxygen and changes into ashes, carbon dioxide, and water vapor. If you were to measure the mass of wood before the fire and the ashes and gases produced after the fire, the total mass after the fire would be the same. Why is this?

....

....

....

3. **CCC Energy and Matter** A neighbor wants to use his backyard garden to conduct an investigation of how tomato plants use specific amounts of carbon dioxide and water to grow at a certain rate. Is this a good idea? Explain.

....

....

....

....

....

....

....

4. **SEP Develop Models** The chemical equation below is written with molecular models in place of chemical formulas. On the left is a carbon (C) atom and a molecule of oxygen. On the right is a molecule of carbon dioxide. Write a description of the visual model.

....

....

Quest CHECK-IN

In this lesson, you learned about the law of conservation of mass and how to model chemical reactions using equations. You also learned about different types of reactions and the characteristics of open and closed systems.

Draw Conclusions What type of system should your pack use—an open system or a closed system? Explain.

....

....

....

HANDS-ON LAB

Pack Building

Go online to download the lab worksheet. Build your pack from your design. Then test it to determine whether it is safe and easy to use.

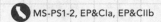
MS-PS1-2, EP&CIa, EP&CIIb

MAKING WATER SAFE TO DRINK

How do you transform dirty water into water you can drink? You engineer it! A portable water purification system may be the answer.

The Challenge: To turn contaminated water into drinkable water in remote areas of the world.

Phenomenon Clean drinking water is essential for people to survive. However, in many places around the world, people have little or no access to clean water. Their water is a mixture of H_2O, particles of soil or waste, and other substances that are not safe to drink, such as lead. It is estimated that more than 780 million people—or 1 in 9 people in the world—do not have access to clean water.

Water purification systems used to be large, heavy, and expensive to operate. But engineers have developed water purification systems that you can carry in your hand. Filters remove the large particles and other compounds that are dissolved or suspended in the water. Additionally, chemicals in these systems undergo chemical reactions that kill bacteria and viruses. These systems remove most of the contaminants from dirty water and make it safe and drinkable.

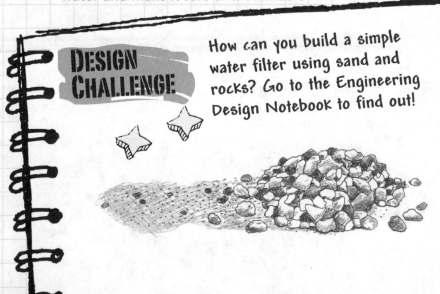

DESIGN CHALLENGE How can you build a simple water filter using sand and rocks? Go to the Engineering Design Notebook to find out!

INTERACTIVITY
Find out more about different contaminants and the methods to remove them.

Water from a local stream is convenient, but it may contain solutes you would never want to drink! Water filtration systems can remove harmful solutes and cause chemical changes that kill bacteria.

HANDS-ON LAB

uInvestigate Discover how to make plastic from starch.

 MS-PS1-3 Gather and make sense of information to describe that synthetic materials come from natural resources and impact society. (Also **EP&CIa, EP&CIIb**)

Connect It !

✏ **Many items you consume every day contain a yellow coloring agent called** *tartrazine*—**the powder shown here. Describe each item by writing** *natural* **or** *artificial* **under the image.**

SEP Construct Explanations What other products do you think contain tartrazine? Explain your reasoning.

....

....

....

Defend Your Claim Some studies have indicated that tartrazine may complicate asthma and cause allergic reactions. Do you think that products containing tartrazine should be used by consumers? Explain why or why not.

....

....

Synthetic Materials

Chemical reactions are constantly happening all around you in nature. Many of the products of naturally occurring reactions have properties that are useful to humans. For instance, plants perform photosynthesis, a chemical reaction that releases oxygen, which you need to survive.

However, not all of the chemicals and materials that humans use come directly from naturally occurring reactions. Instead, they are products of chemical reactions people induce. Such reactions start with substances found in nature, but they result in new materials being formed. For example, glass is made from sand and other minerals that are melted together.

Chemicals and resources made by humans are called **synthetic** materials. Synthetic materials, such as the tartrazine in **Figure 1**, have a wide variety of uses that benefit individuals and society as a whole. Synthetic fertilizers have greatly increased the productivity of farmland. Synthetics have allowed great advances in engineering and technology, which have affected all branches of science. Chemists are always trying out new chemical reactions to produce new materials for society's ever-changing needs.

INTERACTIVITY

Engage in a class discussion about synthetic materials in your everyday life.

Making Colors in the Lab
Figure 1 Tartrazine is a synthetic coloring agent. It is used in products ranging from foods to medicines and cosmetics.

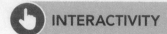
INTERACTIVITY

Explore the relationship between natural resources and synthetics in medicine.

Academic Vocabulary

Replicate means to copy or repeat. Use the word replicate in a sentence.

....

....

Natural Resources as Building Blocks All the useful materials you benefit from are synthesized from natural resources. A **natural resource** is anything naturally occurring in the environment that humans use. These resources may be pure elements, simple molecules, or complex molecules. Many natural resources are only available in limited quantities, which may restrict the use of them in synthetic materials. In addition, depleting natural resources harms the environment.

Chemists assemble synthetic materials in an ordered set of steps, using chemical reactions to create the desired material. The process can be **replicated** at a later time or by another lab to produce the same results. In just the way you would build a house one brick at a time, a chemist synthesizes a material by adding molecular "blocks" one step at a time. You build the house by moving the bricks into place by hand. The chemist relies upon chemical reactions to move molecules into place.

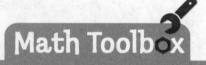

Math Toolbox
Nutrient Concentration

Vitamin C is an essential nutrient for a healthy, functioning body. This vitamin can be obtained from food sources or in a synthetic form in a tablet.

A tablet with a mass of 500 mg contains about 450 mg of synthetic vitamin C.

A 180-g (180,000-mg) orange contains about 106 mg of vitamin C.

1. Use Ratio Reasoning Compare the concentrations of vitamin C in the tablet and in the orange. To determine the concentration, calculate the percent of each object that is made up of vitamin C.

....

....

....

....

2. SEP Interpret Data About how many oranges would you need to eat to get the same amount of vitamin C in one tablet?

....

3. Analyze Quantitative Relationships A carton of California navel oranges has a mass of 18.2 kilograms. How much vitamin C do the oranges contain?

....

Properties of Pure Substances

Every pure substance has characteristic physical and chemical properties that you use to identify a quantity of it. Under given conditions, substances react in characteristic, predictable ways. Then atoms of the original substances regroup into molecules of new substances with physical and chemical properties different from the original substances. For example, sodium is a soft metal with a low melting point, and chlorine is a toxic gas. When sodium burns in chlorine gas, the product formed by the reaction is sodium chloride (NaCl), which is table salt. The reaction of two substances produces a new material with completely different properties, and you can eat it!

With the knowledge of how they chemically react with each other, chemists can combine substances to produce materials that serve particular functions. This isn't to say that all synthetic materials are created on purpose, as shown in **Figure 2**.

Accidental Synthetics

Figure 2 Many synthetic materials were created accidentally in the lab. Use what you know about each of these products to write their properties.

SEP Evaluate Information Use library or Internet resources to check your answers and find out more about each synthetic product. Make sure to evaluate the credibility of the sources you use.

Synthetic and How It Was Discovered	Useful Properties
Superglue In the 1940s, a chemist working on plastic gun sights synthesized a material called cyanoacrylate that frustratingly stuck to everything it touched. A few years later, the chemist came up with an important purpose for the sticky material. 	
 **Nonstick Coating** In the 1930s, a chemist working on a new refrigerant came back to his lab to find small white flakes in a container instead of a gas he had been experimenting with. The chemist had unintentionally synthesized a new nonstick substance.	
Artificial Sweetener In the late 1800s, a chemist was working on an experimental compound. Forgetting to wash his hands before eating, he noticed that everything he ate tasted very sweet. 	

Polymers

Polymers Many natural and artificial materials are made of **polymers**. Polymers are long chains of molecules that are made up of repeating units called monomers. Polymers occur naturally and have been used by people for centuries. They include wool, silk, rubber, and cellulose. The microscopic structure of polymers gives them many different and important macroscopic properties, such as strength, flexibility, and elasticity, all due to the structure of long molecule chains. Polymers that don't occur naturally are synthesized in large quantities to provide clothes, building materials, and many other material goods. Plastic water bottles and toothbrushes (**Figure 3**) are made of polymers.

The most common synthetic polymers are plastics. Plastics are moldable substances that are strong but flexible. These synthetic materials are usually made from petroleum, a natural resource. While plastics have revolutionized our lives, they also are generally very slow to biodegrade. They contribute to pollution when they are not recycled.

✓ **CHECK POINT** **Summarize** Why do chemists synthesize polymers in the lab?

....

....

....

The Structure of Polymers

Figure 3 The composition of a polymer such as a plastic may be very simple, but the size of molecules may be huge, containing millions of atoms!

SEP Develop Models Use the model of the monomer to create a model of a polymer.

Monomer

Polymer

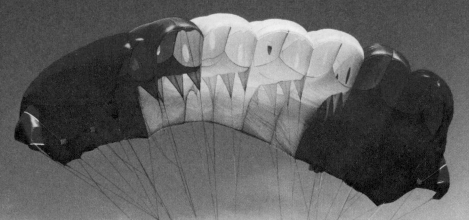

Impact of Synthetic Materials

Synthetic materials allow very large numbers of people to be clothed, housed, and fed. Many of the medical, technological, and societal advances that have occurred during the last 200 years are due in large part to synthetic materials.

Synthetic Fibers Naturally occurring fibers such as cotton, wool, and silk have been used for thousands of years, but they can be expensive. In part, that is because each can be grown or raised only in certain parts of the world. Synthetic fibers, such as acrylic, nylon, polyester, spandex, and rayon, last longer, dry more quickly, and clean more easily than natural fibers, although they often burn more easily. In addition, they generally are much less expensive to produce.

Synthetic Foods Synthetic food products include flavorings, colorings, and preservatives. Vanilla beans grow in only a few places such as Mexico and Madagascar. World demand for flavoring could not be met with vanilla beans, but vanillin is a synthetic flavor produced as substitute for the vanilla flavor. Many foods you eat would spoil quickly without synthetic preservatives. And yet, some preservatives have been found to cause health problems. Superior properties and low cost are great benefits of synthetic products, but some come with health risks that limit their usefulness.

Producing and Using Synthetic Food Products	
Benefits	**Drawbacks**

INTERACTIVITY

Describe the impact of synthetics on society.

Nylon
Figure 4 The polymer nylon is used to make parachutes because of its strength and resistance to tearing.

Literacy Connection

Evaluate Information
Suppose you were asked to research information about a potentially dangerous synthetic food product. How would you evaluate the credibility of the sources you found?

....

....

....

....

Preserving Food
Figure 5 Potassium sorbate is a synthetic food preservative often used in cheese, yogurts, and other dairy products to prevent mold growth. In the table shown, identify some benefits and drawbacks of producing and using synthetic food products.

Synthetic Medicines If you have ever taken medicine for an illness, you have likely benefited from chemical synthesis in the form of pharmaceuticals. Many synthetic chemicals are used to cure or reduce the effects of diseases and illnesses. Many medical compounds have been discovered in plants. Chemists can determine the chemical formula of these natural compounds and then produce them in large amounts and in safer forms through chemical synthesis. *Digitalis lanata,* shown in **Figure 6**, produces a compound that benefits cardiac patients. However, the plant is highly toxic to humans and animals. Chemists have isolated and synthesized the compound, called digoxin, which provides the benefits without the toxic side effects.

Synthetic Fuels Because it is a limited resource, petroleum will one day become too expensive to use as fuel. Cars and trains can run on electricity, but how will planes and boats be powered? Synthetic fuels of many kinds are made through chemical reactions. Chemists have been exploring how to synthesize resources such as plants, animal oils, coal, algae, or other materials into fuels.

☑ CHECK POINT **Evaluate Information** A website publishes an article arguing that synthetic materials do not benefit society because they are created in a lab. Does the evidence support the conclusion? Do you think the website is a reliable source? Explain.

....

....

....

....

Safer Synthetics

Figure 6 This plant is *Digitalis lanata,* also known as Grecian foxglove. It is poisonous and considered an invasive species in California. Chemists, however, have been able to synthesize a useful compound contained in it. As with any medicine, digoxin required thorough testing before it gained government approval for treating heart disease.

Digoxin Tablets
125 micrograms
28 tablets
For oral use

MS-PS1-3, EP&CIa, EP&CIIb

1. Identify What is a synthetic material?

....

....

....

2. Write Informative Texts What type of change must occur for pure substances to combine into new materials? Name a few kinds of synthetic materials that can be produced by this type of change.

....

....

....

....

....

3. CCC Patterns What is the difference between the structures of monomers and polymers?

....

....

....

....

4. CCC Structure and Function Describe how the structure of polymers helps to make them useful materials.

....

....

....

....

....

....

5. SEP Engage in Argument How would you respond to a friend's claim that chemists don't know what to expect when synthesizing new materials?

....

....

....

....

....

....

....

Quest CHECK-IN

In this lesson, you learned how chemists produce synthetic materials. You also investigated how synthetic materials have affected society.

SEP Communicate Information What are some of the benefits and drawbacks of using synthetic materials, such as plastic bags, in your pack design?

....

....

....

....

HANDS-ON LAB

Heat It Up or Ice It Down

Go online to download the lab worksheet. Run through the design cycle again. Modify your your pack to make sure it meets the criteria of the challenge. Then demonstrate your final version.

37

 MS-PS1-2, MS-PS1-5

Evidence-Based Assessment

Burning fossil fuels makes a lot of carbon dioxide (CO_2) gas that enters the atmosphere. About one-fourth of the CO_2 is absorbed by Earth's oceans. Once the CO_2 dissolves in the seawater, it can react with water (H_2O) to produce carbonic acid (H_2CO_3). The data table lists some of the properties of CO_2, H_2O, and H_2CO_3.

Properties of Compounds			
	Carbon Dioxide (CO_2)	**Water (H_2O)**	**Carbonic Acid (H_2CO_3)**
Density*	$0.00198 g/cm^3$	$1.000 g/cm^3$	$2.54 g/cm^3$
Melting Point	$-56.6°C$	$0°C$	$856°C$
Boiling Point	$-78.5°C$ (sublimes)	$100°C$	Not applicable
Solubility	Soluble in water	Not applicable	Soluble in water

* Densities taken at standard temperature and pressure

1. SEP Construct Explanations A student mixes carbonic acid with water. When the solution is heated, the water evaporates and carbonic acid is left as a whitish-gray solid. Explain whether or not a chemical change has taken place.

....

....

....

....

....

2. CCC Scale What will the particles that make up carbonic acid do as the solution changes from a liquid to a solid?
A. slow down
B. break bonds
C. stop vibrating
D. avoid collisions

3. SEP Develop Models ✏️ Draw a model that represents how one molecule of CO_2 and one molecule of H_2O yields one molecule of H_2CO_3. Have you lost any atoms of carbon, hydrogen, or oxygen? Explain.

5. CCC Systems Clams, snails, and oysters make their own shells out of calcium carbonate ($CaCO_3$). $CaCO_3$ can be dissolved by carbonic acid. Over time, how might carbonic acid in the oceans affect a food web that contains these animals?

....

....

....

....

....

....

....

....

....

Quest FINDINGS

Complete the Quest!

Determine the best way to present your design to the class and demonstrate the effectiveness of your pack.

Apply Concepts In this Quest, you dissolved salts in water to cause your pack to heat up or cool down. How might using different substances in the pack increase its effectiveness? How did testing and redesign improve your pack?

4. SEP Cite Evidence Based on the model that you drew, and the data table provided, provide two pieces of evidence that suggest a chemical reaction is occurring between dissolved CO_2 and H_2O in the ocean.

....

....

....

....

....

....

....

....

....

👆 **INTERACTIVITY**

Reflect on Your Pack

MS-PS1-2

Evidence of Chemical Change

How can you **determine** when a **chemical reaction** has occurred?

Background

Phenomenon Quiet on the set! You have been asked to create a video for a science channel to show and explain the differences between physical and chemical changes. In this investigation, you will observe how different substances interact. You will use this information to develop a script for the video that explains how to determine when a chemical change has occurred.

Materials

(per group)

- 3 100-mL beakers
- baking soda (1 teaspoon)
- vinegar (10 mL)
- potato (2-cm cube)
- hydrogen peroxide (25 mL)
- sugar (1 teaspoon)
- iodine (10 mL)
- 3 plastic spoons
- graduated cylinder

Safety

Be sure to follow all safety guidelines provided by your teacher. The Safety Appendix of your textbook provides more details about the safety icons.

Design an Experiment

HANDS-ON LAB

ⁱⁿDemonstrate Go online for a downloadable worksheet of this lab.

☐ 1. Design a procedure using the listed materials that lets you observe interactions of the pairs of substances listed in the table. Here are some questions that might help you to write your procedures:

- At what points in each experiment might you need to make observations?

- What evidence will you specifically look for?

- When is the best time to make your prediction?

- How will you determine whether the interaction has resulted in a physical or chemical change?

- How might you determine when a reaction is complete?

Interactions		
Interaction 1	**Interaction 2**	**Interaction 3**
baking soda and vinegar	sugar and iodine	potato and hydrogen peroxide

☐ 2. Record your predictions and observations in the data table.

☐ 3. 🤚 Get your teacher's approval of your procedure. Then run your experiments.

Procedure

Data Table

Interaction	Prediction	Observations
1		
2		
3		

Analyze and Interpret Data

1. CCC Patterns What similarities and differences did you observe among the three interactions?

....

....

....

2. Make Observations In each case, how did the properties of the substances before the interaction compare to the properties of the substances after the interaction?

Interaction 1:

....

....

Interaction 2:

....

....

Interaction 3:

....

....

3. Apply Scientific Reasoning Which of the three interactions resulted in chemical changes? Were your predictions correct? Explain how observing the properties of substances before and after the interactions helped you to determine whether a chemical change occurred.

....

....

....

....

....

....

....

4. SEP Construct Explanations With your group, use the data and your observations from your experiment to develop a video script. Write it in your notebook. Your script should identify the substances in each interaction, demonstrate the interaction, and then explain how to determine whether a chemical reaction has occurred.

Cell Processes

What is the role of photosynthesis in cycling matter and energy through organisms?

MS-LS1-6 Construct a scientific explanation based on evidence for the role of photosynthesis in the cycling of matter and flow of energy into and out of organisms.

MS-LS1-7 Develop a model to describe how food is rearranged through chemical reactions forming new molecules that support growth and/or release energy as this matter moves through an organism.

EP&CIIIa Students should be developing an understanding that natural systems proceed through cycles and processes that are required for their functioning.

EP&CIIIb Students should be developing an understanding that human practices depend upon and benefit from the cycles and processes that operate within natural systems.

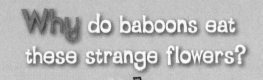

Why do baboons eat these strange flowers?

HANDS-ON LAB

uConnect Explore the type of energy used to power a calculator.

What questions do you have about the phenomenon?

_____

_____

_____

_____

_____

_____

_____

_____

_____

Quest PBL

What is causing the organisms in the greenhouse to fail?

Figure It Out A horticulturalist working at a botanical garden notices that a greenhouse has been damaged during a storm. The glass shutters that allow air to enter the greenhouse are stuck and won't open. The horticulturalist knows that when a greenhouse can't function properly, there is a negative impact on the plants. In this problem-based Quest activity, you will investigate the factors that may be harming the plants and birds in a neighbor's greenhouse. By applying what you've learned in each lesson to digital activities, you will determine what is going wrong in the greenhouse. Then, in the findings activity, you will develop a plan of action that explains why your recommended steps will solve the problem.

👆 **INTERACTIVITY**

🕐 MS-LS1-6, MS-LS1-7

Problem in the Greenhouse

NBC LEARN ▶ VIDEO

After watching the Quest Kickoff video, which explores vertical farming, consider whether starting a vertical farm at your school would be worthwhile. What are some possible benefits? What are some possible drawbacks? Record your ideas below.

....

....

....

....

....

....

....

Quest CHECK-IN

IN LESSON 1

What is necessary for photosynthesis to take place? Explore the components necessary for photosynthesis.

👆 **INTERACTIVITY**

Photosynthesis in the Greenhouse

Quest CHECK-IN

IN LESSON 2

What factors affect cellular respiration? Analyze graphs and data to determine how levels of oxygen and carbon dioxide can impact cellular respiration.

👆 **INTERACTIVITY**

Respiration in the Greenhouse

Greenhouses allow plants to grow even in cold weather.

Quest CHECK-IN

IN LESSON 2

Why is the cycling of matter important in the greenhouse? Model how matter cycles to help determine what might be happening to the plants and birds.

👆 **INTERACTIVITY**

Cycling of Matter in the Greenhouse

Quest FINDINGS

Complete the Quest!

Create a plan of action, including a diagram, to identify the steps your neighbor can take to solve the greenhouse problem.

👆 **INTERACTIVITY**

Reflect on the Problem in the Greenhouse

47

① Photosynthesis

HANDS-ON LAB

uInvestigate Explore why one stage of photosynthesis can take place in the dark.

MS-LS1-6 Construct a scientific explanation based on evidence for the role of photosynthesis in the cycling of matter and flow of energy into and out of organisms.

MS-LS1-7 Develop a model to describe how food is rearranged through chemical reactions forming new molecules that support growth and/or release energy as this matter moves through an organism.

Connect It!

✏️ **In the boxes, write the direct source of energy for each organism.**

SEP Evaluate Evidence Which of the organisms shown does not eat another organism for food?

....

Apply Scientific Reasoning What do you think would happen to each species if the water became too cloudy for sunlight to penetrate?

....

....

....

....

Living Things and Energy

Off the Pacific coast, from Alaska to California, sea urchins graze on kelp beds under water. A sea otter begins the hunt for lunch as they always have and hopefully always will. The otter will take urchins off kelp to eat them at the surface.

Both the sea urchins and the otter in **Figure 1** use the food they eat to obtain energy. Every living thing needs energy. All the cells in every organism need energy to carry out their functions, such as making proteins and transporting substances into and out of the cell. Energy used by living things comes from their environment, similar to the raw materials cells use to function. Meat from the sea urchin provides the otter's cells with energy, while kelp provides energy for the cells of the sea urchin. Where does the energy in the kelp come from? Plants, algae, phytoplankton (floating algae), and some microorganisms including bacteria, obtain their energy differently. These organisms use the energy from sunlight to make their own food.

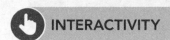

INTERACTIVITY

Identify what items are considered food.

Energy for Life

Figure 1 All living things—such as California sea otters, sea urchins, and kelp—need energy to survive.

CCC Cause and Effect What would likely happen to the kelp if the otters died off?

....

....

....

....

kelp

sea urchins

otter

Summarize Text In your own words, summarize the main idea of the passage on this page.

....

....

....

....

....

....

....

Energy From the Sun Cells capture energy in sunlight and use it to make food in a process called **photosynthesis.** The term *photosynthesis* comes from the Greek words *photos*, which means "light," and *syntithenai*, which means "putting together." Plants and other photosynthetic organisms link molecules together into useful forms using photosynthesis.

Nearly all living things obtain energy directly or indirectly from the sun's energy. This energy is captured from the sunlight during photosynthesis. In **Figure 2,** the leaf obtains energy directly from sunlight because plants use sunlight to make their own food during photosynthesis. When you eat an apple, you get energy from the sun that has been stored in the apple. You get the sun's energy indirectly from the energy that the apple tree gained through photosynthesis.

An Energy Chain

Figure 2 The energy of sunlight passes from one organism to another.

Explain Phenomena 🖉 Draw arrows showing the flow of energy from the sun.

Making and Obtaining Food Plants make their own food through the process of photosynthesis. **Autotrophs**, or producers, are able to create their own food in the form of glucose, an energy-giving sugar. Plants and algae, as well as some bacteria, are autotrophs. An organism that cannot make its own food, such as the sea urchin or otter, is a consumer, or a **heterotroph.** Many heterotrophs, like the fox in **Figure 3**, obtain food by eating other organisms. Some heterotrophs, such as fungi, absorb their food from other organisms.

Reflect How is sunlight important to plant growth? In your science notebook, list some questions you have about the effects of sunlight on growing plants.

☑ CHECK POINT **Summarize Text** What is the difference between heterotrophs and autotrophs?

....

....

....

Model It !

Trace Energy to the Source

Figure 3 A California gray fox captures and eats prey like rabbits and hares that depend on plants for food.

SEP Develop Models ✏ Draw a diagram that tracks how the sun's energy gets to the fox. In your diagram, label each organism as a heterotroph or an autotroph.

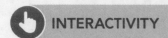
INTERACTIVITY

Describe the cycling of matter and energy that occurs during photosynthesis.

Investigate Explore why one stage of photosynthesis can take place in the dark.

Student Discourse

After reading about Stage 1 of photosynthesis and completing **Figure 4**, form a small group with classmates. Write down two questions about Stage 1. Then each group member should offer a question for the group to discuss.

Photosynthesis

Photosynthesis is a chemical reaction in plants that uses light energy to convert certain types of matter into another they can use as food. It takes place mostly in chloroplasts, as shown in **Figure 4**. When plants use the sun's energy to convert carbon dioxide from the atmosphere and water into sugar, oxygen is produced. Because photosynthesis is a chemical reaction, several different factors affect the rate of chemical change. The availability of sunlight, water, and carbon dioxide are all factors required for photosynthesis.

Stage 1: Trapping the Sun's Energy

Chloroplasts, the green organelles in plant cells, use chlorophyll to absorb sunlight during the first stage of photosynthesis. The green color comes from pigments, which are colored chemical compounds that absorb light. The green photosynthetic pigment found in the chloroplasts of plants, algae, and some bacteria is **chlorophyll**.

Picture solar cells in a solar-powered calculator. Chlorophyll functions in a similar way. Chlorophyll captures light energy that the chloroplast uses to create oxygen and sugar (**Figure 4**).

During Stage 1, sunlight splits water molecules in the chloroplasts into hydrogen and oxygen. The hydrogen combines with other atoms during Stage 2 and the oxygen is released into the environment as a waste product. A product is the substance formed after a reaction takes place. Some oxygen gas exits a leaf through openings on the leaf's underside. Almost all the oxygen in Earth's atmosphere is produced by living things through the process of photosynthesis.

Photosynthesis: Stages 1 and 2

Figure 4 Photosynthesis takes place in the chloroplasts. Specialized structures in each chloroplast contain chlorophyll, a green pigment that captures light energy.

Translate Information ✏️ Add labels to the arrows in the diagram to indicate whether water, carbon dioxide, sugar, or oxygen is entering or leaving.

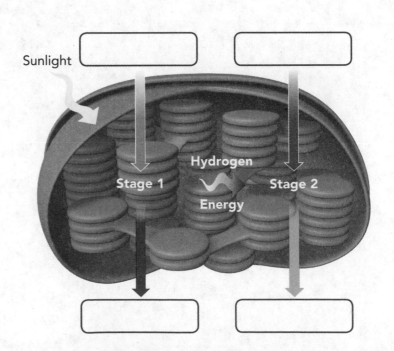

Stage 2: Making Food

In Stage 2 of photosynthesis, cells produce sugar. Sugars are carbon-based organic molecules that are useful for storing chemical energy or for building larger molecules. Glucose, which has the chemical formula $C_6H_{12}O_6$, is one of the most important sugars produced in photosynthesis. The energy stored in the chemical bonds of glucose allows cells to carry out vital functions.

The production of glucose is shown in **Figure 5.** Hydrogen (H) that came from splitting water molecules in Stage 1 is one reactant, the substance undergoing a change during a reaction. The other reactant is carbon dioxide (CO_2) from the air. Carbon dioxide enters the plant through the small openings on the underside of each leaf and moves into the chloroplasts. Powered by the energy captured in Stage 1, hydrogen and carbon dioxide undergo a series of reactions to produce glucose.

☑ **CHECK POINT** **Integrate with Visuals**
✏ On the picture, write R in the circles for the two raw materials, or reactants, of photosynthesis, E in the circle for the energy source, and P in the circles of the two products.

Light energy

Oxygen

Carbon dioxide

Glucose

Water

The Big Picture of Photosynthesis
Figure 5 This view of photosynthesis is from outside the plant. Plant cells also break down glucose to release the energy they need to grow and reproduce.

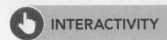
INTERACTIVITY

Determine what factors influence photosynthesis in modern and ancient plants.

Expressing Photosynthesis

The events of photosynthesis that lead to the production of glucose can be expressed as the following chemical **equation**:

$$\text{light energy} + 6\,CO_2\ \text{(carbon dioxide)} + 6\,H_2O\ \text{(water)} \longrightarrow C_6H_{12}O_6\ \text{(glucose)} + 6\,O_2\ \text{(oxygen)}$$

Academic Vocabulary

How is a chemical equation similar to a mathematical equation, and how do they model a natural phenomenon?

....

....

....

....

....

....

....

Notice that six molecules of carbon dioxide and six molecules of water are in the equation to the left of the arrow. These compounds are raw materials, or reactants. One molecule of glucose and six molecules of oxygen are on the right side of the arrow. These compounds are products. An arrow, which means "yields," points from the reactants to the products. Energy is not a reactant, but it is written on the left side of the equation to show that it is used in the reaction. There are the same number of atoms of each element on both sides of the equation—no matter is gained or lost.

Plant cells use some glucose produced in photosynthesis for food. The cells break down sugar molecules in a process called cellular respiration. The energy released from glucose can be used to carry out a plant's functions (**Figure 6**), such as growth. Other glucose molecules are stored for later use. When you eat food from plant roots, such as potatoes or carrots, you are eating the plant's stored energy.

✔CHECK POINT **Determine Central Ideas** What happens to glucose and oxygen that is produced by plants during photosynthesis?

....

....

....

Photosynthesis Is the Key

Figure 6 Green plants use the sugars produced in photosynthesis in many ways.

Interpret Diagrams ✐ Label the leaves, roots, and seeds in the diagram. Then fill in the boxes with some of the ways plants use the products of photosynthesis.

Importance of Plant Cells

Plant cells were the first cells to be seen with a microscope. Because plant cell walls are like rigid boxes, plant cells do not burst when placed in an aquatic environment. The ability to store water is one reason that marshes are so important (**Figure 7**). During storms with heavy rainfall, such as hurricanes, marsh plants soak up water. For this reason, marshland is considered a natural flood control.

Plants and algae that live in water absorb about one sixth of all the sun's energy that falls on Earth. Ocean plants play an essential role in recycling oxygen. In fact, 85 percent of the oxygen in Earth's atmosphere comes from ocean plants. They perform photosynthesis much like land plants. They collect the sun's energy and take in carbon dioxide. They always have water. They use these reactants to produce food (energy) for themselves and to release oxygen into the water for use by other organisms.

Marsh Plants

Figure 7 The marsh in the Vic Fazio Yolo Wildlife Area is managed to help protect Sacramento, California, from flooding. It also provides prime habitat to nearly 200 species of birds and other wetland wildlife.

SEP Construct Explanations How do marshes control flooding?

....

....

Math Toolbox

All in the Balance

The photosynthesis equation states that 6 CO_2 and 6 H_2O molecules combine to form 1 $C_6H_{12}O_6$ molecule and 6 O_2 molecules. For every 6 carbon dioxide molecules, the reaction produces 1 glucose molecule.

1. **Represent Relationships** Write an equation using two variables to model how many glucose molecules are produced when there are 6 CO_2 molecules. Use x for the number of glucose molecules and y for the number of CO_2 molecules.

   ....

2. **Analyze Relationships** ✏ Calculate how many glucose molecules are produced when there are 6, 12, 18, and 24 CO_2 molecules. Plot these points on the graph. What is the relationship between the two variables?

   ....

   ....

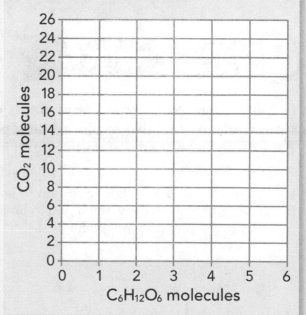

Proportion Relationship

(graph: y-axis labeled CO_2 molecules, 0 to 26; x-axis labeled $C_6H_{12}O_6$ molecules, 0 to 6)

MS-LS1-6, MS-LS1-7

1. Analyze Systems Where does a plant get the energy necessary to drive the chemical reaction in photosynthesis?

....

....

2. SEP Cite Evidence How do you know an organism is a heterotroph? Name three heterotrophs.

....

....

....

....

....

3. SEP Construct Explanations How does chlorophyll help the functioning of chloroplasts?

....

....

....

....

....

4. CCC Cause and Effect What are the roles of light, carbon dioxide, and water molecules in the production of food and oxygen in photosynthesis?

....

....

....

....

....

....

....

....

....

....

....

....

....

....

....

....

Quest CHECK-IN

In this lesson, you learned how plants capture energy from the sun. You also explored how plants use carbon dioxide to produce food and oxygen in the process of photosynthesis.

Identify Variables Why is it important to understand the process of photosynthesis when trying to understand what is wrong with the plants in the greenhouse?

....

....

....

INTERACTIVITY

Photosynthesis in the Greenhouse

Go online to explore how temperature, carbon dioxide levels, and light intensity can affect a plant's ability to carry out photosynthesis.

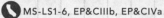
Engineering Artificial
PHOTOSYNTHESIS

How do you make photosynthesis more efficient?
You engineer it!

The Challenge: To create a more efficient form of photosynthesis.

Phenomenon Photosynthesis is an important process for all life on Earth. However, it isn't very efficient. Only 1 percent of the sunlight that hits a leaf is used during the process of photosynthesis.

Scientists at the Joint Center for Artificial Photosynthesis (JCAP) in California hope to engineer ways of improving that efficiency. Founded in 2010 by the U.S. Department of Energy, the center has one main goal: to find a way to produce fossil fuel alternatives using just sunlight, water, and carbon dioxide. The center is led by a team of scientists and researchers at the California Institute of Technology in partnership with the Lawrence Berkeley National Laboratory. JCAP's facilities have state-of-the-art tools and technologies at its disposal for scientists to conduct investigations and experiments of just about any kind as they relate to photosynthesis.

In his 2011 State of the Union address to Congress, President Obama singled out the work of JCAP researchers: "We're issuing a challenge. We're telling America's scientists and engineers that if they assemble teams of the best minds in their fields, and focus on the hardest problems in clean energy, we'll fund the Apollo projects of our time. At the California Institute of Technology, they're developing a way to turn sunlight and water into fuel for our cars."

 VIDEO
Examine how the different parts of an artificial leaf work.

JCAP scientists are developing solar fuel generators (shown here) that mimic the process of photosynthesis with greater efficiency.

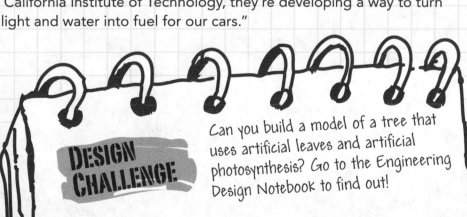

DESIGN CHALLENGE

Can you build a model of a tree that uses artificial leaves and artificial photosynthesis? Go to the Engineering Design Notebook to find out!

LESSON
(2) Cellular Respiration

HANDS-ON LAB

uInvestigate Examine a product of cellular respiration.

MS-LS1-6 Construct a scientific explanation based on evidence for the role of photosynthesis in the cycling of matter and flow of energy into and out of organisms.

MS-LS1-7 Develop a model to describe how food is rearranged through chemical reactions forming new molecules that support growth and/or release energy as this matter moves through an organism.

Connect It !

✏ **Draw arrows on Figure 1 to show the flow of energy from the food into the bikers, and then out into the environment as heat and motion.**

Construct a Graph ✏ Sketch on the graph to show how the bikers' energy level may change over time as they start biking, stop for a snack, start biking again, and finish their ride.

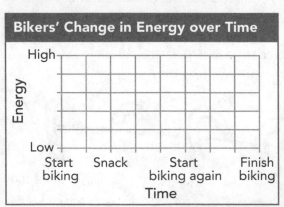

Bikers' Change in Energy over Time

High

Energy

Low

Start biking — Snack — Start biking again — Finish biking

Time

Energy and Cellular Respiration

You and your friend have been biking all morning. The steepest part of the road is ahead. You'll need a lot of energy to get to the top! The food shown in **Figure 1** will provide some of that energy.

Plants and animals break down food into small, usable molecules, such as glucose. Energy stored in these molecules is released so the cell can carry out functions. **Cellular respiration** is the process in which oxygen and glucose undergo a complex series of chemical reactions inside cells, releasing energy. All living things need energy. Therefore, all living things carry out cellular respiration.

Using Energy A hot water heater stores hot water. To wash your hands, you turn on the faucet and draw out the needed hot water. Your body stores and uses energy in a similar way. When you eat, you add to your body's energy account by storing glucose, fat, and other substances. When cells need energy, they "draw it out" by breaking down the energy-rich compounds through cellular respiration.

Respiration People often use the word *respiration* when they mean *breathing*, the physical movement of air in and out of your lungs. In the study of the life sciences, however, respiration and breathing are not interchangeable. Breathing brings oxygen into your lungs. Cells use oxygen in cellular respiration. Exhaling removes the waste products of that process from your body.

HANDS-ON LAB

Investigate how yeast carry out cellular respiration.

Food for Energy
Figure 1 Biking takes a lot of energy! Your body uses cellular respiration to get energy from the food you eat, such as trail mix.

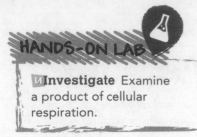
Academic Vocabulary

How can the terms *produce* and *source* be used to describe a nation's economy?

....

....

....

....

Releasing Energy

Figure 2 Cellular respiration takes place in two stages.

Integrate Information ✏
Fill in the missing terms in the spaces provided.

Cellular Respiration Process
Like photosynthesis, cellular respiration is a two-stage process. **Figure 2** shows both stages of cellular respiration. Stage 1 occurs in the cell's cytoplasm, where glucose is broken down into smaller molecules. Oxygen is not involved in this stage, and only a small amount of energy is released. Stage 2 occurs in a mitochondrion and uses oxygen. The smaller molecules produced in Stage 1 are broken down even more. Stage 2 releases a great deal of energy that the cell can use for all its activities.

Cellular Respiration Equation
The raw materials for cellular respiration are glucose and oxygen. Heterotrophs get glucose from consuming food. Autotrophs carry out photosynthesis to **produce** their own glucose. Air is the **source** of oxygen. The products of cellular respiration are carbon dioxide and water. Although respiration occurs in a series of complex steps, the overall process can be summarized in the equation:

$$\underset{\text{glucose}}{C_6H_{12}O_6} + \underset{\text{oxygen}}{6\,O_2} \longrightarrow \underset{\text{carbon dioxide}}{6\,CO_2} + \underset{\text{water}}{6\,H_2O} + \text{energy}$$

Stage 1 In the cytoplasm, ... is broken down into smaller molecules, releasing a small amount of ....

Stage 2 In the ...., the smaller molecules react, producing ...., water, and large amounts of ....

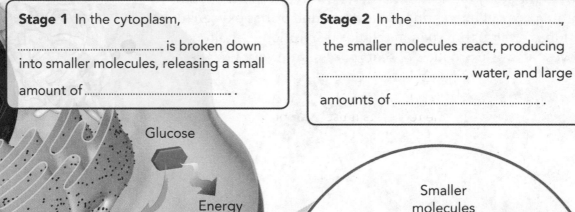

Glucose

Energy

Smaller molecules

Mitochondrion

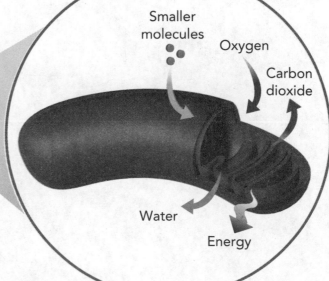

Smaller molecules

Oxygen

Carbon dioxide

Water

Energy

Role of Mitochondria

It may be a small organelle, but the mitochondrion (plural, mitochondria) is well known as the cell's powerhouse. The function of the mitochondrion is to create large amounts of energy. In **Figure 2**, notice how the mitochondrion is structured. The folds inside the organelle create more surface area. Chemical reactions occur on these folds. Because of this increased surface area, many more chemical reactions can occur. In turn, more energy is created. Cells that need a great deal of energy may have thousands of mitochondria. If a cell needs more energy to survive, it can create more mitochondria.

Not all organisms use glucose and oxygen to carry out cellular respiration. Some organisms rely on a type of cellular respiration that uses fructose instead of glucose to create energy. For this chemical reaction, they do not need oxygen to break down the fructose.

✓ CHECK POINT **Determine Conclusions** Think about the job of the mitochondria. Which cells in your body would you expect to have the most mitochondria? Explain your reasoning.

....

....

Literacy Connection

Translate Information ✏️ In **Figure 2**, circle the folds in the mitochondrion that increase the organelle's surface area.

📓 **Reflect** "Respiration" can also refer to breathing. Is some sort of "breathing" required for cellular respiration to occur? Do plants "breathe"?

Model It!

SEP Develop Models ✏️ Create a model of a mitochondrion showing its roles during cellular respiration. Show both the activities that occur there and all the reactants it uses and products released there.

Related Processes

Figure 3 Carbon dioxide and oxygen cycle through cellular respiration and photosynthesis.

1. **CCC Relate Structure and Function** ✎ Label the diagram to complete each of the processes.

2. **Connect to the Environment** Why do you think it is important for us to decrease the release of carbon dioxide gas even though autotrophs take it in during photosynthesis?

....

....

....

....

....

....

....

Comparing Two Energy Processes

If you think the equation for cellular respiration is the opposite of the one for photosynthesis, you're right! Photosynthesis and cellular respiration can be thought of as opposite processes. The two processes form a cycle, keeping the levels of oxygen and carbon dioxide molecules relatively stable in Earth's atmosphere. As shown in **Figure 3**, living things cycle both gases repeatedly. The energy released through cellular respiration is used or lost as heat. Matter and energy is neither created or destroyed in this cycle.

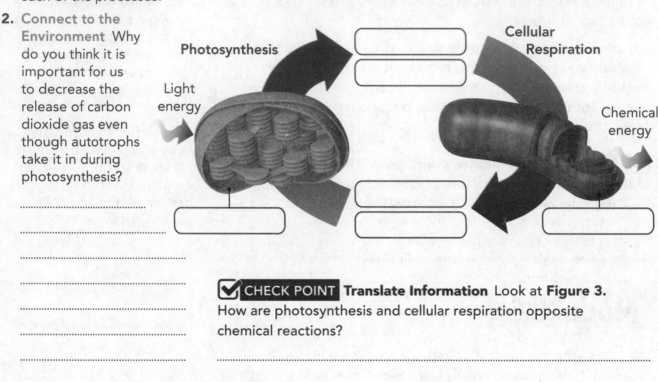

☑ **CHECK POINT** **Translate Information** Look at **Figure 3**. How are photosynthesis and cellular respiration opposite chemical reactions?

....

....

Fermentation

Yeast, bacteria, and your own muscle cells can release energy from food without oxygen. The release of energy from food without using oxygen is called **fermentation**. Fermentation is very useful in environments with limited oxygen, such as in the intestines. However, fermentation releases much less energy than cellular respiration with oxygen.

Alcoholic Fermentation When you eat a slice of bread, you are eating a product of fermentation. Alcoholic fermentation takes place in live yeast cells—unicellular fungi—and in other single-celled organisms. This type of fermentation produces alcohol, carbon dioxide, and a small amount of energy. Bakers use these products of fermentation. Carbon dioxide creates gas pockets in bread dough. This causes the dough to rise.

Lactic Acid Fermentation Have you ever run as fast and hard as you could, like the sprinter in **Figure 4**? Although you started to breathe faster, your muscle cells used up oxygen faster than it could be replaced. Without enough oxygen, fermentation takes place. Your body supplies energy to your muscle cells by breaking down glucose without using oxygen. A compound called lactic acid is a product of fermentation in muscles. One popular misconception is that lactic acid "builds up in the muscles" and causes "muscle burn" as well as any lingering soreness. However, lactic acid actually fuels your muscles and goes away shortly after the workout.

☑ CHECK POINT **Determine Central Ideas** How does fermentation that causes dough to rise differ from fermentation in muscles?

....

....

....

....

....

standing

jogging

sprinting

Running Out of Oxygen

Figure 4 Your breathing and blood circulation can supply enough oxygen for cellular respiration when you exercise gently. During a sprint, your cells run low on oxygen and switch to lactic acid fermentation for energy.

SEP Evaluate Evidence 🖊 For each activity, label the source of energy for the muscle cells. Is it oxygen or lactic acid?

63

MS-LS1-6, MS-LS1-7

1. CCC Construct Explanations Do plants and animals both use cellular respiration? Explain.

Yes. They both need glucose.

2. Apply Concepts How do heterotrophs get energy? Explain.

They get energy from other animals.

3. SEP Develop Models 🖊 In the space below, sketch and label a diagram showing the relationship between photosynthesis and cellular respiration.

Quest CHECK-INS

In this lesson, you learned about the process of cellular respiration, in which the cells of an organism use sugar and oxygen to produce energy and carbon dioxide.

Evaluate Why is it important to consider the process of cellular respiration when determining what is going wrong in the greenhouse?

👆 INTERACTIVITIES

Respiration in the Greenhouse; Cycling of Matter in the Greenhouse

Go online to learn about the factors that affect the process of cellular respiration. Consider how these factors might explain why the greenhouse is failing. Then analyze the data from the sensors in the greenhouse. Make some generalizations about the data to help you begin developing your action plan.

Too Much of a Good Thing

CONNECT TO YOU

Should schools sell candy and soft drinks to students?

Almost everyone loves sweets. After all, they taste really good. But sugary foods have negative effects on our health. The sugar we eat is broken down by our cells for energy. Under normal circumstances, cells break down all the sugar they receive and produce enough energy. However, what happens when cells get too much sugar?

Our bodies need one important sugar to survive—glucose—and it's serious fuel for your brain, too. So how can sugar hurt us? The problem is that we do not limit our sugar intake to what occurs naturally in fruits and vegetables. Most of the sugar we eat is sugar that gets added to foods and beverages like sodas and energy drinks. And there is way too much of it.

One health consequence of eating too much sugar is obesity, which puts people at a higher risk for diabetes or even a heart attack. Another consequence is "brain decay." Some studies show that mental decline is one outcome for people who develop diabetes. Then there is cancer. Other studies show that people who consume high levels of sugar have a much higher risk of getting cancer.

The average teen consumes 22–34 teaspoons of added sugars each day. This 12-ounce serving of soda has about 10 teaspoons of sugar. The recommended amount of added sugars for teens each day is no more than 9 teaspoons.

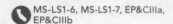

MS-LS1-6, MS-LS1-7, EP&CIIIa, EP&CIIIb

Evidence-Based Assessment

In late 2013, California was in the midst of a severe drought. Farms, ranches, and vineyards were suffering. Agriculture is an important part of the state's economy and it was suffering. In January 2014, the governor issued an official State of Emergency, with the goal of easing the impact of the drought on citizens, crops, and the environment. It stated that:

> State agencies, led by the Department of Water Resources, will execute a statewide water conservation campaign to make all Californians aware of the drought and encourage personal actions to reduce water usage. This campaign will coordinate with local water agencies, [and] . . . call on Californians to reduce their water usage by 20 percent.

Fortunately, the drought ended in late 2016. Governor Brown lifted the State of Emergency in April 2017. Estimating annual runoff helps to analyze the moisture level of an area to determine a drought. *Annual runoff* is water that is released by the land, or "runs off," in one year. Runoff is mostly precipitation that remains after water has evaporated, been used by plants, and seeped into soil. Runoff will make its way to bodies of water.

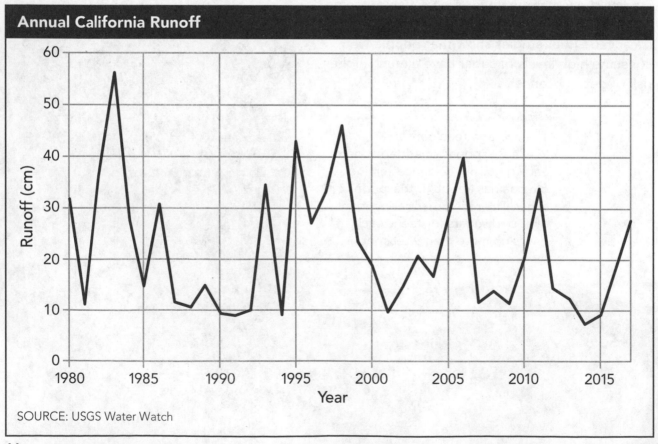

Annual California Runoff

SOURCE: USGS Water Watch

Use the graph to answer the questions.

1. **SEP Analyze Data** What do the data indicate about California's climate?
   A. It is steadily becoming wetter.
   B. It is steadily becoming drier.
   C. It has wetter and drier cycles.
   D. It does not change.

2. **SEP Evaluate Evidence** Where does the water a land plant uses for photosynthesis come from? Why would that water be scarce during a drought? Select the answers to make the statement true.

   The water comes from ....
   A. evaporation   B. condensation
   C. precipitation

   During a drought, soil is ....
   A. wetter   B. drier

   due to ....
   A. excess rain or snow
   B. little rain or snow
   C. less water vapor in the air

3. **SEP Construct Explanations** If a plant is considered drought-resistant, does it require more water or less water to perform photosynthesis? Explain.

   ....

   ....

   ....

4. **Analyze Phenomenon** Low-lying areas like river valleys can dry out in droughts but may also flood in unusually rainy periods. Suppose you were a valley tomato farmer in California. Based on your knowledge of photosynthesis and the data, would you buy seeds that were regular, drought-resistant, flood-resistant, or some combination? Explain.

   ....

   ....

   ....

   ....

   ....

   ....

5. **Connect to Environmental Principles and Concepts** The processes of photosynthesis and cellular respiration are continually cycling matter: carbon dioxide, water, and oxygen. How can a drought affect both processes in that cycle? Select all that apply.

   ☐ Less available water means photosynthesis slows down.

   ☐ Less oxygen is produced, so more cellular respiration can occur.

   ☐ Less oxygen is produced and cellular respiration slows down.

   ☐ More cellular respiration occurs, producing more carbon dioxide.

   ☐ Less carbon dioxide in the atmosphere can slow photosynthesis in plants.

   ☐ Plants have more carbon dioxide and photosynthesis occurs at a faster rate.

Quest FINDINGS

Complete the Quest!

Create a plan of action to identify the steps your neighbor can take to solve the greenhouse problem.

CCC Analyze Systems Photosynthesis and cellular respiration play important roles in the cycling of matter and energy on Earth. How are plants and animals dependent on one another for survival?

....

....

....

....

....

👆 **INTERACTIVITY**

Reflect on the Problem in the Greenhouse

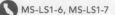

MS-LS1-6, MS-LS1-7

Cycling Energy and
Matter

How can you **model** matter and energy moving **through** a **living system**?

Background

Phenomenon What's the farthest you've ever walked? How did you have the energy to walk that far? You probably know that you get energy from the food you eat. But where did the energy in your food come from? In this investigation, you will demonstrate how matter and energy move through a living system.

Materials

(per group)
- eight test tubes
- two test tube racks
- cardboard box
- four snails
- four Elodea
- for each test tube: approximately 30 mL of deionized water to cover the organisms and 3 mL of bromothymol blue
- grow light

Safety

Be sure to follow all safety guidelines provided by your teacher. The appendix of your textbook provides more details about the safety icons.

Plan Your Investigation

HANDS-ON LAB

υDemonstrate Go online for a downloadable worksheet of this lab.

1. Knowing that bromothymol blue turns yellow in the presence of carbon dioxide, discuss as a group how to design an investigation to answer these questions:

   • How can we determine whether cellular respiration or photosynthesis is taking place in an organism?

   • Using these two organisms, how can we model an ecosystem in which matter is recycled?

2. Predict any outcomes you expect and determine what you will be observing and what data you will be recording. Create a data table in the space provided.

3. Put the following items in each test tube as indicated:

   • **Suggestion:** Number the test tubes from 1–8. Arrange the odd-numbered test tubes in one group and the even-numbered test tubes in another group.

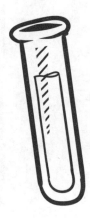

Test Tubes	Items
1 and 2	water only
3 and 4	two snails
5 and 6	two strands of Elodea
7 and 8	two snails and two strands of Elodea

Snails are animals that conduct cellular respiration.

4. In the space provided, briefly describe your investigation and the procedure you will follow.

5. Conduct your investigation. Remember to record your observations in your data table. Make observations after 24 hours as well.

Elodea is a plant that conducts photosynthesis in light. It also conducts cellular respiration.

Procedure

Data Table

Analyze and Interpret Data

1. **Identify Variables** The control group of this experiment consisted of the test tubes filled with only water. What is the purpose of this control group?

....

....

2. **SEP Analyze Data** Consider the two test tubes that contained only the strands of Elodea. What accounts for the difference in the colors of the liquid in the test tubes after 24 hours?

....

....

....

....

....

3. **Claim** What gas was present in the test tubes containing both Elodea and snails after 24 hours?

....

4. **Evidence** What evidence supports the presence of your claim in the test tubes containing both Elodea and snails?

....

5. **Reasoning** Explain how your evidence supports your claim for the test tubes containing both Elodea and snails.

....

....

....

....

6. **SEP Develop Models** Sketch a simple diagram of a snail and a strand of Elodea. Model how carbon dioxide and oxygen cycles between the plants and snails.

Minerals and Rocks in the Geosphere

How can you model the cycling of Earth's materials?

MS-ESS2-1 Develop a model to describe the cycling of Earth's materials and the flow of energy that drives this process.

MS-ESS3-1 Construct a scientific explanation based on evidence for how the uneven distributions of Earth's mineral, energy, and groundwater resources are the result of past and current geoscience processes.

What caused this rock to look like this?

HANDS-ON LAB

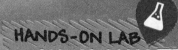

☑**Connect** Explore and model Earth's structure.

What questions do you have about the phenomenon?

....
....
....
....
....
....
....
....
....
....

Quest PBL

How can you depict Earth processes in a movie script?

Figure It Out A movie producer is working on an exciting new adventure film. Much of the action takes place not in space, not on Earth, but *under* the surface of Earth. The producer wants to present a realistic view of this world, so she hires a science consultant to help get the facts right. In this problem-based Quest activity, you will help evaluate and revise movie scripts whose plots involve action that takes place within Earth. Based on your research and understanding of Earth's structure, you will suggest changes that reflect accurate science. In the Findings activity, you will reflect on how accurately movies depict scientific facts.

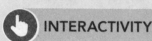 **INTERACTIVITY**   MS-ESS2-1

Science in the Movies

NBC LEARN ▶ VIDEO

After watching the Quest Kickoff video and reacting to some movie scenes, think about a scientific falsehood that you have seen in a movie. How do you suggest changing the script to reflect the science accurately?

The scene and its false science

....

....

....

....

How the scene should be changed

....

....

....

....

Quest CHECK-IN

IN LESSON 1
What is the structure of Earth's mantle and core? How could a movie accurately depict these regions inside Earth?

👆 **INTERACTIVITY**

The Deep Drill

Quest CHECK-IN

IN LESSON 2
How do stalactites and stalagmites form? Model the formation of these structures.

HANDS-ON LAB

Make Your Own Stalactites and Stalagmites

Quest CHECK-IN

IN LESSON 3
What are the three types of rocks and how do they form? Consider how different types of rock form and represent that information accurately in a movie script.

👆 **INTERACTIVITY**

Rocky Business

The 1959 movie *Journey to the Center of the Earth* was based on Jules Verne's novel, published in 1864. In the story, a professor and several other characters travel through the center of Earth, entering through a volcano in Iceland and exiting through a volcano in Italy.

Quest CHECK-IN

IN LESSON 4

What processes affect rock formation? Understand different rock cycle processes and appropriately depict those processes in a script.

👆 **INTERACTIVITY**

The Rock Cyclers

Quest FINDINGS

Complete the Quest!

Now that you have revised movie scripts to be more scientifically accurate, consider how you will view the science in other movies differently.

👆 **INTERACTIVITY**

Reflect on Science in Movies

1 Earth's Interior

HANDS-ON LAB

ưInvestigate Explore how convection works.

 MS-ESS2-1 Develop a model to describe the cycling of Earth's materials and the flow of energy that drives this process.

Connect It!

What do you observe about the rock shown in Figure 1?

Determine Differences How do the xenoliths compare to the surrounding rock?

....

Apply Scientific Reasoning How might xenoliths help geologists understand Earth's interior?

....

....

Learning About Earth's Interior

How do we study Earth's interior and connect those interior processes to things we see or experience on Earth's surface? This question is difficult to answer because geologists are unable to see deep inside Earth. However, geologists have found other ways to study the unseen interior of Earth. Their methods focus on two main types of **evidence**: direct evidence from rock samples (**Figure 1**) and indirect evidence from seismic waves.

Academic Vocabulary

Suppose you think the air temperature is getting colder. Give two examples of evidence you could use to support your idea.

....

....

....

....

....

....

Rock Hitchhikers

Figure 1 These yellowish-green pieces of rock are *xenoliths*, from ancient Greek words *xeno*, meaning "foreign," and *lith*, meaning "rock." These xenoliths are fragments of peridotite, a rock that forms at least 50 to 60 kilometers deep inside Earth. They were picked up and carried to the surface by melted rock that later hardened and formed the grayish surrounding rock.

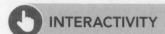
Evidence From Rock Samples

Geologists have drilled holes as deep as 12.3 kilometers into Earth. Drilling brings up many samples of rock and gives geologists many clues. They learn about Earth's structure and conditions deep inside Earth where the rocks are formed. In addition, volcanoes sometimes carry rocks to the surface from depths of more than 100 kilometers. These rocks provide more information about Earth's interior, including clues about how matter and energy flow there. Some rocks from mountain ranges show evidence that they formed deep within Earth's crust and surfaced when mountains formed. Also, in laboratories, geologists have used models to recreate conditions similar to those inside Earth to see how those conditions affect rock.

Evidence From Seismic Waves

To study Earth's interior, geologists also use an indirect method. When earthquakes occur, they produce **seismic waves** (SIZE mik). Geologists record the seismic waves and study how they travel through Earth. The paths of seismic waves reveal where the makeup or form of the rocks change, as shown in **Figure 2**.

Waves

Figure 2 Earthquakes produce different types of seismic waves that travel through Earth. The speed of these waves and the paths they take give geologists clues about the structure of the planet's interior.

Make Observations
Compare and contrast the paths that P-waves and S-waves take through Earth. How do you think this information helps geologists understand Earth's interior?

....
....
....
....
....
....
....

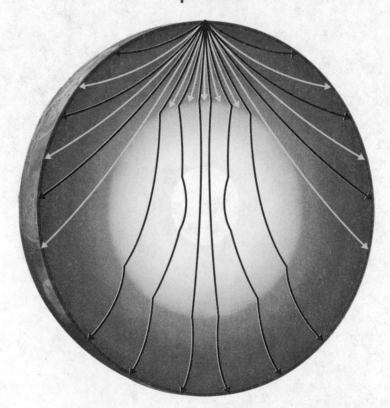

Earthquake epicenter

⟶ P-waves travel through solids and liquids.

⟶ S-waves only travel through solids.

Earth's Layers

After many years of research, scientists today know that Earth's interior is made up of three main layers: crust, mantle, and core. These layers vary greatly in thickness, composition, temperature, and pressure.

Pressure results from a force pressing on an area. Within Earth's interior, the mass of rock that is pressing down from above causes an increase of pressure on the rocks below. The deeper inside Earth's interior, the greater the pressure becomes. Pressure inside Earth increases much like water pressure in the swimming pool increases as you dive down deeper, as in **Figure 3**.

The temperature inside Earth increases as depth increases. Just beneath Earth's surface, the surrounding rock is cool. At about 20 meters down, the rock starts to get warmer. For every 40 meters of depth from that point, the temperature typically rises 1 degree Celsius. The rapid rise in temperature continues for several tens of kilometers. Eventually, the temperature increases more slowly, but steadily. The high temperatures inside Earth are mostly the result of the release of energy from radioactive substances and heat left over from the formation of Earth 4.6 billion years ago.

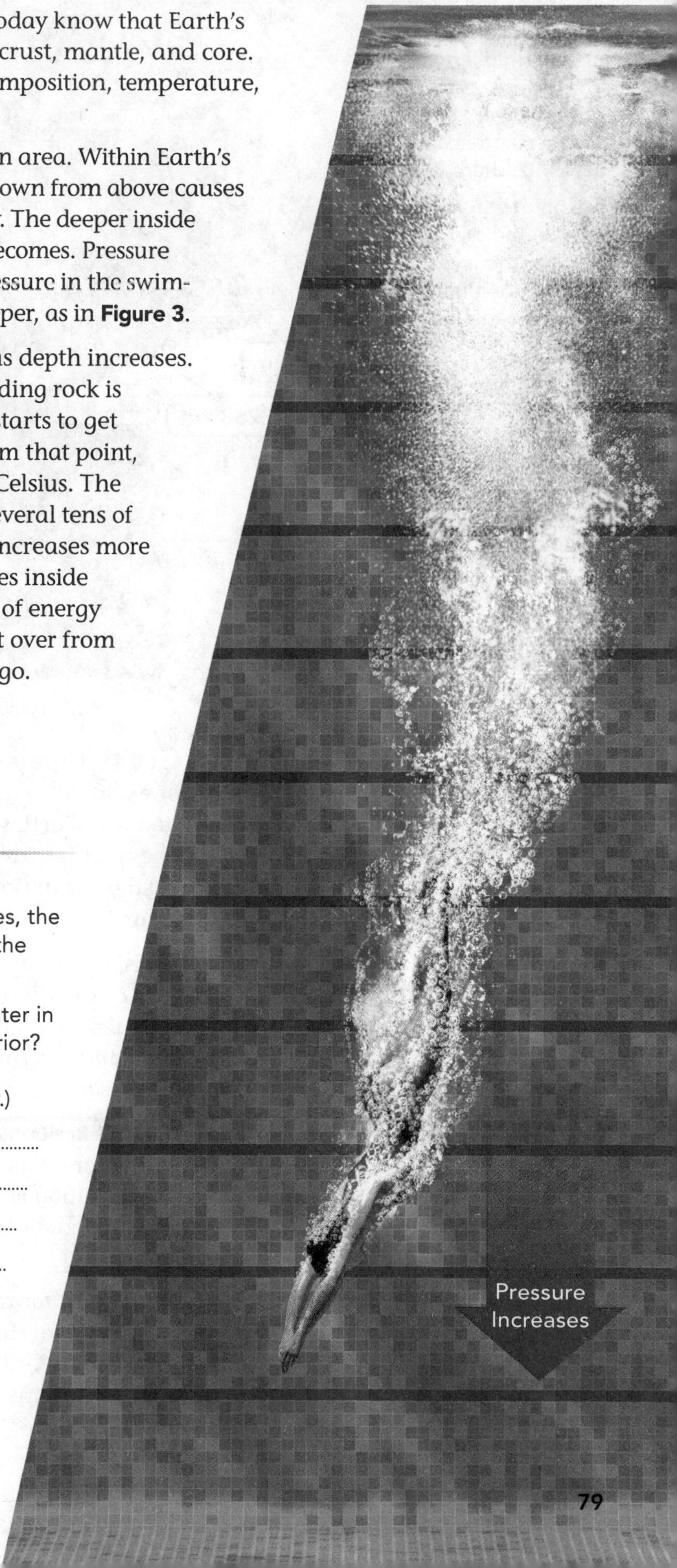

Pressure and Depth

Figure 3 The deeper that the swimmer goes, the greater the pressure on the swimmer from the surrounding water.

1. **Compare and Contrast** How is the water in the swimming pool similar to Earth's interior? How is it different? (*Hint:* Consider both temperature and pressure in your answer.)

   ....

   ....

   ....

   ....

   ....

2. **CCC Use Proportional Relationships** At what location in the pool would the water pressure be greatest?

   ....

Pressure Increases

79

Earth's Layers

Figure 4 The crust and uppermost mantle make up the rigid lithosphere. The lithosphere rests on the lower, softer part of the mantle called the asthenosphere.

Translate Information

✎ Use the diagram to identify the layers and contrast how rigid they are.

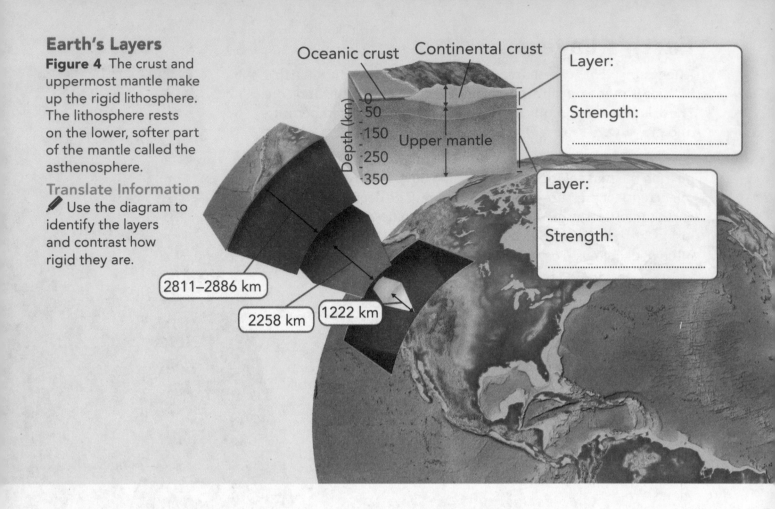

Oceanic crust   Continental crust

Depth (km)

0
-50
-150   Upper mantle
-250
-350

Layer:
....
Strength:
....

Layer:
....
Strength:
....

2811–2886 km

2258 km   1222 km

The Crust Have you ever hiked up a mountain, toured a mine, or explored a cave? During each of these activities you interacted with Earth's **crust**, the rock that forms Earth's outer layer. The crust is a layer of solid rock that includes both dry land and the ocean floor. The main **elements** of the rocks in the crust are oxygen and silicon.

The crust is much thinner than the layers beneath it. In most places, the crust is between 5 and 40 kilometers thick. It is thickest under high mountains, where it can be as thick as 80 kilometers, and it is thinnest beneath the ocean floor. There are two types of crust: oceanic crust and continental crust.

The crust that lies beneath the ocean is called oceanic crust. The composition of all oceanic crust is nearly the same. Its overall composition is much like basalt, with small amounts of ocean sediment on top. Basalt (buh SAWLT) is a dark, fine-grained rock.

Continental crust forms the continents. It contains many types of rocks. But overall the composition of continental crust is much like granite. Granite is a rock that usually is a light color and has coarse grains.

The Mantle Directly below the crust, the rock in Earth's interior changes. Rock here contains more magnesium and iron than does the rock above it. The rock below the crust is the solid material of the **mantle**, a layer of hot rock. Overall, the mantle is nearly 3,000 kilometers thick.

The uppermost part of the mantle is brittle rock, like the rock of the crust. Both the crust and the uppermost part of the mantle are strong, hard, and rigid. Geologists often group the crust and uppermost mantle into a single layer called the lithosphere. As shown in **Figure 4**, Earth's lithosphere is about 100 kilometers thick.

Below the lithosphere, the material is increasingly hotter. As a result, the part of the mantle just beneath the lithosphere is less rigid than the lithosphere itself. Over thousands of years, this part of the mantle may bend like a metal spoon, but it is still solid. This solid yet bendable layer is called the asthenosphere.

Beneath the asthenosphere is the lower mantle, which is hot, rigid, and under intense pressure. The lower mantle extends down to Earth's core.

INTERACTIVITY

Examine the different layers of Earth.

Math Toolbox

Temperature in Earth's Layers

1. **Construct Graphs** Use the data in the table to complete the line graph.

2. **Interpret Graphs** How does temperature change with depth in Earth's mantle?

....

....

....

....

Depth (km)	Temperature (°C)
500	1,600°C
1,000	1,800°C
1,500	2,200°C
2,000	2,500°C
2,500	2,900°C

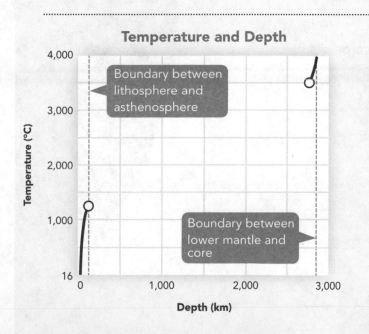

Temperature and Depth

Boundary between lithosphere and asthenosphere

Boundary between lower mantle and core

Temperature (°C): 16, 1,000, 2,000, 3,000, 4,000

Depth (km): 0, 1,000, 2,000, 3,000

Student Discourse In a small group, discuss the best ways to remember the differences among Earth's layers: depth, relative thickness, composition, solid/liquid. Record one or two of the most useful ways.

The Core Below the mantle is Earth's dense core. Earth's core occupies the center of the planet. It consists of two parts, a liquid outer core and a solid inner core. The outer core is 2,260 kilometers thick. The inner core is a solid ball with a radius of about 1,220 kilometers. Therefore, the total radius of the entire core is approximately 3,480 kilometers.

The **outer core** is a layer of molten metal surrounding the inner core. Despite enormous pressure, the outer core is liquid. The **inner core** is a dense ball of solid metal. In the inner core, extreme pressure squeezes the atoms of iron and nickel so much that they cannot spread out to become liquid despite the extremely high temperatures.

Model It

1. **SEP Evaluate Evidence** Label Earth's layers, and use the text on the page to fill in the table with details about the layers.

	Thickness	Composition	Solid/Liquid
Crust:			
Mantle:			
Outer core:			
Inner core:			
Total:	6,370 km		

2. **Compare and Contrast** Pick any two points inside Earth and label them A and B. Record their locations.

My Point A is in the ....

My Point B is in the ....

Compare and contrast Earth at those two points.

....

....

....

....

....

....

Currently, most evidence suggests that both parts of the core are mostly made of iron and nickel. Scientists have found data suggesting that the core also contains smaller amounts of oxygen, sulfur, and silicon.

✓ CHECK POINT **Cite Textual Evidence** What are the similarities and differences between the inner core and the outer core?

....

....

....

Modeling Earth's Interior
Figure 5 Earth is divided into distinct layers. Each layer has its own characteristics.

Movement in Earth's Mantle

Recall that Earth's mantle and core are extremely hot. Heat is a form of energy that flows. It transfers from matter at a higher temperature to matter at a lower temperature. The transfer of heat in the mantle drives a process called convection. This process is how matter cycles and energy flows through Earth's interior as well as its surface.

Movement of Energy When you heat water on a stove, the water at the bottom of the pot gets hot and expands. As the heated water expands, its density decreases. Less-dense fluids flow up through denser fluids.

Movement of Energy in Hot Springs

Figure 6 Hot springs are common in Yellowstone National Park. Here, melted snow and rainwater seep far below the crust into the mantle, where a shallow magma chamber heats the rock of Earth's crust. The rock heats the water to more than 200°C and puts it under very high pressure. This superheated groundwater rises to the surface and forms pools of hot water.

1. **Compare and Contrast** The heated water is (more dense / less dense) than the melted snow and rainwater.

2. **Apply Concepts** What process causes convection currents to form in a hot spring?

....

....

....

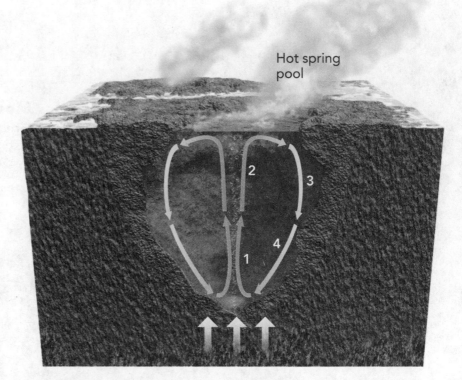

Hot spring pool

The warm, less dense water moves upward and floats over the cooler, denser water. Near the surface, the warm water cools, becoming denser again. It sinks back down to the bottom of the pot. Here, the water heats and rises again. The flows shown in **Figure 6** that transfer heat within matter are called convection currents. Heating and cooling of matter, changes in matter's density, and the force of gravity combine and set convection currents in motion. Without heat, convection currents eventually stop.

✓ CHECK POINT **Translate Information** What three processes or forces combine to set convection currents in motion?

....

....

....

Movement of Energy in Earth

Heat from the core and from the mantle itself drives convection currents. These currents carry hot, solid rock of the mantle outward and cooled, solid rock inward in a never-ending cycle.

As the oceanic lithosphere cools and sinks, it drives a pattern of mantle convection. The cold lithosphere moves down into the mantle, where it is heated. An upward return flow of hot rock completes the cycle, as shown in **Figure 7**. Over and over, the cycle of sinking and rising takes place. One full cycle takes millions of years. Convection currents are involved in the production of new rock at Earth's surface. There are also convection currents in the outer core.

Literacy Connection

Translate Information
Use the visuals depicting convection to explain how the directions of two side-by-side convection currents can transform the crust.

....

....

....

....

....

....

....

....

Mantle Convection
Figure 7 Complete the model by drawing the missing convection currents.

SEP Use Models Complete the labels by using the terms in the box.

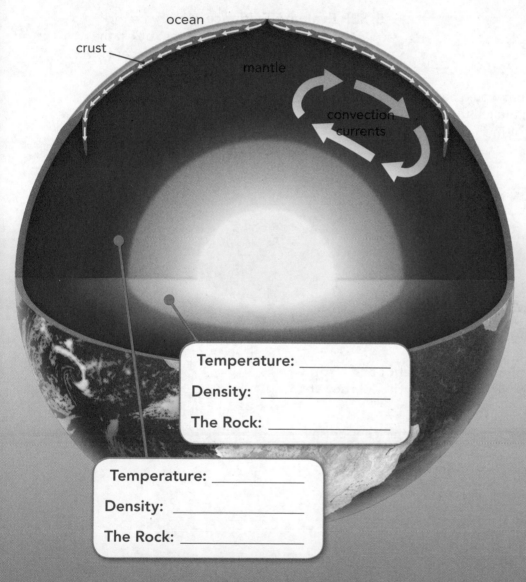

ocean

crust

mantle

convection currents

Temperature: _____

Density: _____

The Rock: _____

Temperature: _____

Density: _____

The Rock: _____

hotter

colder

less dense

more dense

sinks

rises

Write About It How can a solid, such as mantle rock, flow? Think about candle wax. In your science notebook, write a procedure for making candle wax flow. Then list observations of other solids that you have seen flow.

☑ LESSON 1 Check

MS-ESS2-1

1. Communicate Name each layer of Earth, starting from Earth's center.

....

....

....

2. CCC Stability and Change Do pressure and temperature remain constant in Earth's interior? Explain.

....

....

....

....

3. CCC Cause and Effect What would happen to the convection currents in the mantle if Earth's interior cooled down? Why?

....

....

....

....

....

4. SEP Construct Explanations How do changes in temperature cause convection, the movement of material in Earth's interior?

....

....

....

....

....

....

....

5. SEP Evaluate Evidence How is the rock in the deep mantle similar to the rock in the parts of the mantle nearest the surface? How is it different?

....

....

....

....

....

....

....

Quest CHECK-IN

In this lesson, you learned about Earth's interior and also how energy and material move between Earth's interior and its surface.

SEP Engage in Argument Explain why you think it is or isn't important for science fiction films to depict natural processes and geological events as accurately as possible.

....

....

....

....

....

👆 INTERACTIVITY

The Deep Drill

Go online to find out more about Earth's interior structure. Then evaluate the science facts in a movie script.

INTERACTIVITY

Design a satellite that can collect electromagnetic field data.

Examining **Earth's Interior** *from* **Space**

How can you study Earth's interior? You engineer it! Geologists use satellites to help them visualize what they cannot see.

The Challenge: To understand how scientists study what they can't observe directly.

Phenomenon As Earth rotates, its liquid outer core spins. The flow and movement of Earth's oceans also create electric currents that generate secondary magnetic fields. Scientists call this process "motional induction." The European Space Agency (ESA) has launched three satellites into Earth's orbit that are sensitive to these electric currents.

The satellites also tell us many details about the electrical conductivity inside Earth's core—both the liquid of the outer core and the solid metallic sphere found at the center of the planet. A rock's ability to conduct electricity is related to its temperature, mineral composition, and water content. A satellite cannot directly measure these things. However, scientists can now draw reasonable conclusions about them by studying satellite data about the electric currents that flow through and just below Earth's surface.

Swarm Satellites launched in November 2013. The ESA's three-satellite Swarm mission is helping to improve our understanding of Earth's interior by taking measurements of its magnetic fields.

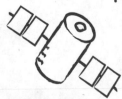

DESIGN CHALLENGE

Can you design your own satellite? Go to the Engineering Design Notebook to find out!

② Minerals

HANDS-ON LAB

ᴎInvestigate Model mineral crystals and observe how they can change.

MS-ESS2-1 Develop a model to describe the cycling of Earth's materials and the flow of energy that drives this process.

MS-ESS3-1 Construct a scientific explanation based on evidence for how the uneven distributions of Earth's mineral, energy, and groundwater resources are the result of past and current geoscience processes.

Connect It !

✏ **Circle two crystals in the photo.**

Relate Change Do you think these crystals formed in conditions that were stable or that changed often? Explain.

....

....

....

....

Defining Minerals

Look at the objects in **Figure 1**. They are solid matter that formed deep beneath Earth's surface. They are beautiful, gigantic crystals of the mineral selenite, which is a form of gypsum. But what is a mineral?

Characteristics A **mineral** is a naturally occurring solid that can form by inorganic processes and has a crystal structure and definite chemical composition. For a substance to be a mineral, it must have the following five characteristics.

Naturally Occurring All minerals are substances that form by natural processes. Gypsum forms naturally from chemical elements that precipitate from water.

Solid A mineral is always a solid, which means it has a definite volume and shape. The particles in a solid are packed tightly together. Gypsum is a solid.

Forms by Inorganic Processes All minerals must be able to form by inorganic processes. That is, they can form from materials that were not a part of living things. Gypsum forms naturally as sulfate-rich solutions evaporate. Some minerals, such as calcite, form from both inorganic and organic processes.

Crystal Structure The particles of a mineral line up in a pattern that repeats over and over again. The repeating pattern of a mineral's particles forms a solid called a **crystal**. The gypsum in the image has a crystal structure.

Definite Chemical Composition A mineral has a definite chemical composition. This means it always contains the same elements in certain proportions. Gypsum always contains calcium, oxygen, sulfur, and hydrogen, in set proportions.

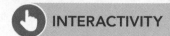
INTERACTIVITY

Explain what the term *mineral* means to you.

Reflect Write down where you recall hearing of minerals before, and the names of any minerals that play a role in your everyday life.

Mineral Giants

Figure 1 Dwarfed by megacrystals of the mineral selenite, miners explore Mexico's Cave of Crystals. Located about 300 meters below Earth's surface, the cave contains some of the largest crystals ever discovered in nature—up to 12 meters long!

INTERACTIVITY

Compare and contrast the different properties of minerals.

Mineral Properties Geologists have identified and named more than 5,000 minerals, though only about 20 make up most of the rocks of Earth's crust. Because there are so many minerals, telling them apart can be challenging. Each mineral has characteristic properties that are used to identify and describe it. **Figure 2** shows some of the properties of the mineral pyrite.

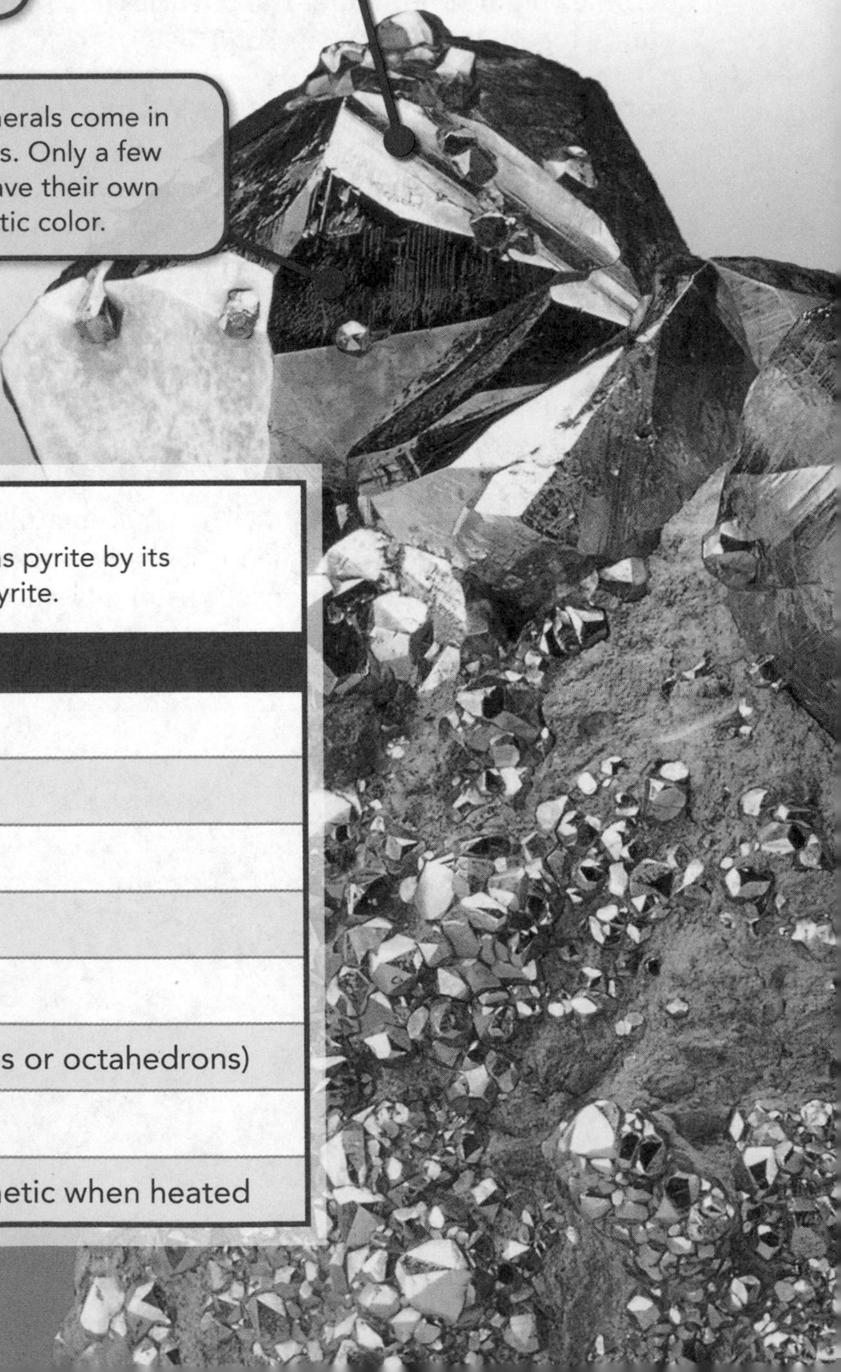
Luster Luster is the term that describes how light reflects from a mineral's surface. Terms used to describe luster include *metallic, glassy, earthy, silky, waxy,* and *pearly.*
Streak The streak of a mineral is the color of its powder. Although the color of a mineral can vary, its streak does not.
Color Minerals come in many colors. Only a few minerals have their own characteristic color.

Identifying Minerals

Figure 2 You can identify a mineral such as pyrite by its properties. Describe the color and luster of pyrite.

Properties of Pyrite	
Color	
Streak	Greenish black
Luster	
Hardness	6–6.5
Density	5 g/cm^3
Crystal structure	Isometric (cubes or octahedrons)
Cleavage or fracture	None; uneven
Special	Becomes magnetic when heated

Density Each mineral has a characteristic density, or mass in a given volume. To calculate a mineral's density, use this formula: Density = Mass/Volume

Cleavage and Fracture A mineral that splits easily along flat surfaces has the property called cleavage. Whether a mineral has cleavage depends on how the atoms in its crystals are arranged. Most minerals do not split apart evenly. Instead, they have a characteristic type of fracture. Fracture describes how a mineral looks when it breaks apart in an irregular way.

Special Properties Some minerals can be identified by special physical properties. For example, calcite bends light to produce double images. Other minerals conduct electricity, glow when placed under ultraviolet light, or are magnetic.

Crystal Structure All the crystals of a mineral have the same crystal structure. Different minerals have crystals that are shaped differently. Geologists classify crystals by the number of faces, or sides, on the crystal and the angles at which the faces meet.

INTERACTIVITY

Analyze mineral properties.

Math Toolbox

Calculate Density

A sample of the mineral cinnabar has a mass of 251.1 g and a volume of 31.0 cm^3.

SEP Use Mathematics What is the density of cinnabar?

....

....

....

....

Hardness The Mohs hardness scale is used to rank the hardness of minerals from 1 being the softest to 10 being the hardest. A mineral can scratch any mineral softer than itself but can be scratched by any mineral that is harder.

Where Minerals Form

Figure 3 ✏ Minerals can form by crystallization of magma and lava or precipitation of materials dissolved in water. Circle the area where you might find a cave with crystals similar to the large crystals shown in **Figure 1**.

HANDS-ON LAB

u Investigate Model mineral crystals and observe how they can change.

Academic Vocabulary

You might be familiar with term *organic food*. How does this meaning of *organic* differ from the scientific meaning?

....

....

....

....

....

Mineral Formation

In general, minerals can form in a few different ways and at different locations at or below Earth's surface (**Figure 3**). Some minerals form from organic processes. Other minerals form from the materials dissolved in evaporating solutions of water. Many minerals form when magma and lava, originally heated by the energy of Earth's interior, cool and solidify. Finally, some minerals form when other minerals are heated or compressed, which causes the material to deform, or change shape, in the process of deformation.

Organic Minerals All minerals can form by inorganic processes. However, many **organic** processes can also form minerals. For instance, animals such as cows and humans produce skeletons made of the mineral calcium phosphate. Ultimately, the energy used to drive the processes of mineral formation in most living things can be traced all the way back to the sun and the plants that use its energy.

Minerals From Solutions Sometimes the elements and compounds that form minerals dissolve in water and form solutions. On Earth's surface, energy from the sun can cause water to evaporate, leaving behind minerals. Water below Earth's surface, which is under intense pressure and at high temperatures, can pick up elements and compounds from surrounding rock. When these elements and compounds leave the water solution through precipitation, crystallization can occur.

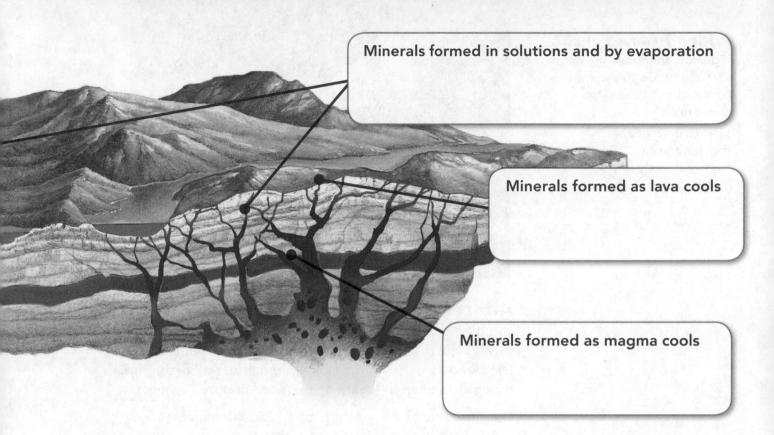

Minerals formed in solutions and by evaporation

Minerals formed as lava cools

Minerals formed as magma cools

Crystallization is the process by which atoms are arranged to form a material that has a crystal structure. Minerals such as halite, calcite, and gypsum form through crystallization when bodies of water on Earth's surface evaporate.

In another example, the huge crystals in **Figure 1** formed from a solution of water heated by energy from Earth's interior that eventually cooled underground. But the process was an extremely long one, taking place over millions of years.

Minerals From Magma and Lava
Many minerals form when hot magma from Earth's interior cools higher in the crust, or when lava cools and hardens on the surface. Crystals form when these liquids cool to a solid state.

The size of the crystals depends on several factors, including the rate at which the melted rock cools. Slow cooling leads to the formation of large crystals, such as coarse quartz and feldspar crystals found in granite that slowly cools underground. Fast cooling leaves very little time for crystals to grow. Lava cools quickly on the surface or under water and forms small crystals, such as pyroxene and fine-grained olivine in basalt rock of the oceanic crust.

☑ CHECK POINT **Translate Information** What type of minerals might a geologist expect to find near the site of an ancient lava flow? Explain.

....

....

A Ring from a Pencil?

Figure 4 Immense pressure and heat in Earth's mantle compacts graphite into diamond.

SEP Construct Explanations Why do diamonds only form in certain spots in the mantle?

....

....

....

graphite

cut diamond

Altered Minerals A change of temperature or pressure can alter one mineral into a new mineral. Graphite, for example, is a soft mineral commonly used in pencils. Diamonds are the hardest known material on Earth. Both minerals, shown in **Figure 4**, are made of pure carbon.

Diamonds form deeper than about 150 kilometers (about 90 miles) beneath Earth's surface within the mantle. At this depth below continental crust, temperatures reach between 900°C to 1,300°C, and the pressure is about 50,000 times greater than at Earth's surface. The intense pressure and high temperature alter the structure of the carbon atoms in graphite, forming diamond.

These diamond zones may also contain magma. Long ago, the pressure that formed diamonds also caused magma to squeeze toward Earth's surface, where it might erupt. Sometimes, diamonds were carried along for the ride. When the magma cooled in pipe-like formations, the diamonds were embedded in this rock.

Model It

Diamond Formation

SEP Develop Models ✏ Use the information in the text and **Figure 3** to draw a diagram that shows how diamonds form. Your model should show and label the following parts of the process:

1. Graphite in the mantle that is under intense pressure becomes diamonds.

2. In the past, magma from the mantle moved quickly toward Earth's surface, forming pipes.

3. The magma cooled with the diamonds trapped within it.

Mineral Distribution

The common minerals that make up the rocks of Earth's crust are found abundantly throughout Earth's surface. Other minerals are much less common because their formation depends on certain materials and conditions that may be limited. Other minerals may form as the result of processes that take a very long time, which will limit where and how much of the mineral can form. The process by which diamonds are formed is one example.

Geological processes often tied to plate tectonics, such as volcanic eruptions or evaporations in ocean basins, can cause certain minerals to collect in concentrated deposits. These deposits, or ores, are mined for the valuable materials they contain. **Figure 6** shows the distribution of some of Earth's mineral resources.

California Gold Rush

Figure 5 The California Gold Rush made the U.S. aware that it had major gold deposits. The U.S. is now the fourth-largest gold-producing nation.

Mineral Resources

Figure 6 The map shows the location of some important mineral resources on Earth.

1. **Translate Information** According to the map, does California have any gold deposits?

....

2. **SEP Construct Explanations** What patterns do you notice in the distributions of minerals on Earth? Explain.

....

....

....

....

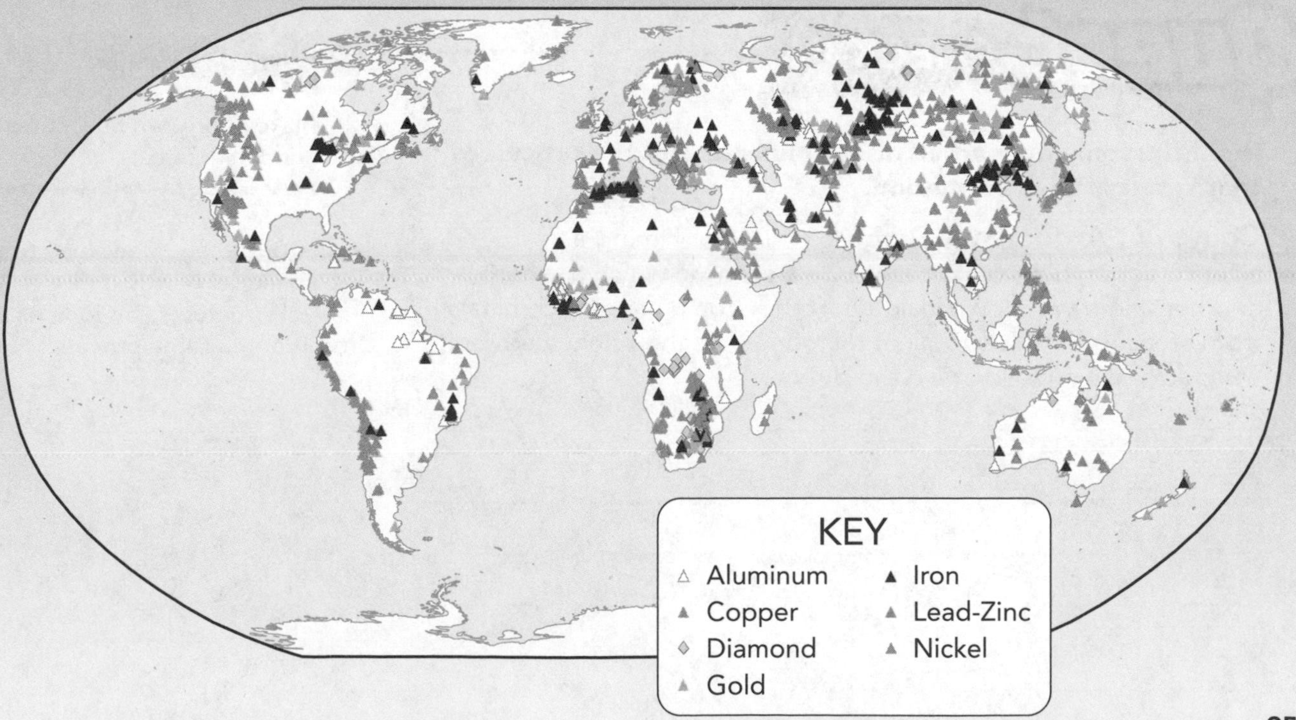

KEY

△ Aluminum
▲ Copper
◆ Diamond
▲ Gold
▲ Iron
▲ Lead-Zinc
▲ Nickel

MS-ESS2-1, MS-ESS3-1

1. Analyze Properties What are some of the properties that geologists use to identify and describe minerals?

....

....

....

2. SEP Construct Explanations Why aren't diamonds found evenly distributed on Earth?

....

....

....

....

....

3. Apply Concepts Amber is a solid material used in jewelry. It forms in nature only by the process of pine tree resin hardening. Explain why you think amber is or is not a mineral.

....

....

....

....

4. CCC Cause and Effect What role does the sun's energy play in the formation of minerals from solutions?

....

....

....

....

....

5. SEP Develop Models ✏ Draw a flow chart or cycle diagram to show one way a mineral gets recycled in nature and forms a new mineral.

Quest CHECK-IN

In this lesson, you learned about minerals and the processes that result in their formation.

Construct Arguments Suppose a director filming a science fiction film wants to include a scene in which the hero and heroine travel down inside Earth to stop a band of criminals from stealing Earth's supply of diamonds. As the science advisor, what advice would you give the director?

....

....

....

....

HANDS-ON LAB

Make Your Own Stalactites and Stalagmites

Go online and download the lab to model how two different crystal structures can form as a result of the same process.

MS-ESS2-1

The Cost of
TECHNOLOGY

Coltan ore before processing to extract tantalum.

You may never have heard of the element tantalum, but you probably use it every day. The electrical properties of tantalum make it a good material to use in capacitors in electronic devices. And it's found in all the smartphones, laptops, and other electronics that billions of people use to stay organized, get work done, and communicate with each other.

Tantalum must be extracted from an ore called coltan. The ore must be mined and refined before the tantalum can be used. By the turn of the 21st century, worldwide demand for electronics reached a peak, which increased demand for tantalum. Prior to 2000, most of the world's tantalum was extracted from coltan mined in Australia and Brazil. These countries have stricter mining regulations, which increases the cost of mining tantalum.

When demand for tantalum exploded, coltan mining increased in the Democratic Republic of Congo (DRC) and neighboring countries in Africa. But the DRC has been torn apart by civil war, which has lured armed coltan miners looking for a fast profit. The government does little to regulate how the coltan is mined. The unregulated, often illegal, mining provides inexpensive tantalum but destroys vital wildlife habitats and helps to fund continued conflict in this war-ravaged country.

MY COMMUNITY

How would you solve the problem of the need for coltan versus the need to source the coltan responsibly? Work in a small group to identify possible solutions. Conduct internet research to find facts and evidence that support your arguments.

These miners search for coltan, iron ore, and manganese at the Mudere mine in eastern Democratic Republic of Congo.

(3) Rocks

HANDS-ON LAB

ʊInvestigate Examine how pressure can change rock.

MS-ESS2-1 Develop a model to describe the cycling of Earth's materials and the flow of energy that drives this process.

Connect It!

✏️ **Draw an outline of what the weathered rock may have looked like 2,000 years ago.**

SEP Construct Explanations How do you think the rock formation will continue to change over time?

....

....

....

....

....

Describing Rocks

In southern Utah, spires and buttes of red sandstone rise up into the sky in Monument Valley (**Figure 1**). To a tourist or other casual observer, these rock formations seem to stand motionless and unchanging. But every moment of every day, forces are at work on these rocks, slowly changing their shapes and sizes. Weathering, erosion, transportation, and deposition all work to wear away and alter the appearance of the rock formations.

Rocks, like the sandstone in Monument Valley, are made of mixtures of minerals and other materials. To describe rocks, geologists observe mineral composition, color, and texture.

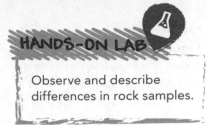

HANDS-ON LAB

Observe and describe differences in rock samples.

Towers of Rock
Figure 1 The striking red color of Monument Valley is the result of iron oxide minerals exposed within the rock.

Granite

Figure 2 Granite is generally made up of only a few common minerals. This coarse granite formed when magma cooled slowly.

Mica

Quartz

Granite

Feldspar

Hornblende

1. **Claim** Circle the best word to complete each sentence.

   Granite is generally (dark / light) in color.

   Granite has a (high / low) silica content.

   The grains in granite are (fine / coarse).

2. **Evidence** What evidence did you use to make your claim?

   ....

   ....

3. **Reasoning** Explain how your evidence supported your claim.

   ....

   ....

   ....

   ....

   ....

Mineral Composition and Color

Some rocks contain only a single mineral. Other rocks contain several minerals. About 20 minerals make up most of the rocks of Earth's crust. These minerals are known as rock-forming minerals.

A rock's color provides clues to the rock's mineral composition. Granite, as shown in **Figure 2**, is generally a light-colored rock that has high silica content, meaning it is rich in the elements silicon and oxygen.

Texture

Most rocks are made up of particles of minerals or other rocks, which geologists call grains. To describe the texture of a rock, geologists use terms that are based on the size, shape, and pattern of the grains. For example, rocks with grains that are large and easy to see are coarse-grained. In fine-grained rocks, grains can be seen only with a microscope.

Origin

Using mineral composition, color, and texture, geologists classify a rock's origin—how the rock formed. Geologists have classified rocks into three major groups based on origin: igneous rock, sedimentary rock, and metamorphic rock.

CHECK POINT **Determine Meaning** *Ignis* means "fire" in Latin. What may be "fiery" about igneous rocks?

....

 INTERACTIVITY

Identify and evaluate the characteristics of different rocks.

Plan It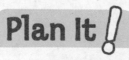

Rocky Observations

As part of a geological investigation you are conducting, you observe three rock samples.

SEP Analyze Data What characteristics would you examine to help you distinguish among the three rocks?

....

....

How Rocks Form

Each type of rock, whether it's igneous, sedimentary, or metamorphic, forms in a different way.

Igneous Rock Rock that forms from cooled magma or lava is **igneous rock** (IG nee us). Igneous rocks can look very different from each other. The temperature and composition of the molten rock determine the kind of igneous rock that is formed.

Igneous rock may form on or beneath Earth's surface from molten material that cools and hardens. Extrusive rock is igneous rock formed from lava that erupted onto Earth's surface. Basalt is the most common extrusive rock, making up a large part of oceanic crust. Igneous rock that formed when magma hardened beneath the surface of Earth is called intrusive rock. The most abundant type of intrusive rock in the continental crust is granite. Granite forms tens of kilometers below Earth's surface and over hundreds of thousands of years or longer. When granite ends up close to the surface, it may be mined for use as road-building material, in a crushed state, or as a building material, in large polished slabs.

The texture of most igneous rock depends on the size and shape of its mineral crystals (**Figure 3**). Rapidly cooling lava found at or near Earth's surface forms fine-grained igneous rocks with small crystals or no minerals at all. Slowly cooling magma below Earth's surface forms coarse-grained rocks, such as granite and diorite, with large crystals. Intrusive rocks have larger grains than extrusive rocks. Extrusive rocks that cool too quickly to form any minerals are called glass.

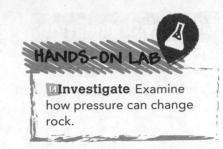

HANDS-ON LAB

☑**Investigate** Examine how pressure can change rock.

Igneous Rock Formation

Figure 3 The texture of igneous rock varies according to how it forms.

SEP Evaluate Evidence ✏ Did the rocks in the photographs form at A or B? Write your answers in the spaces provided.

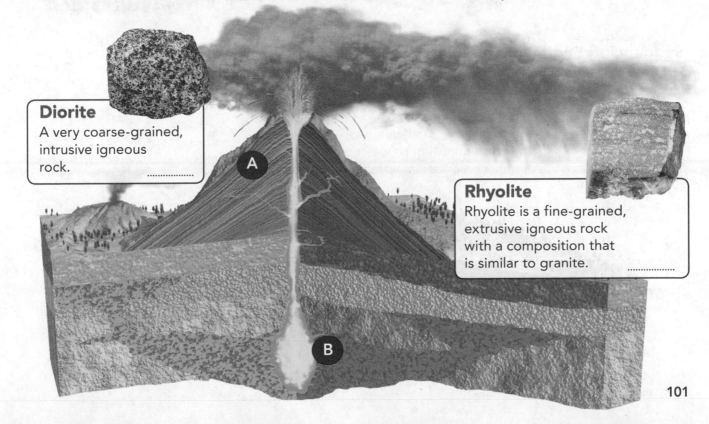

Diorite
A very coarse-grained, intrusive igneous rock. ....

Rhyolite
Rhyolite is a fine-grained, extrusive igneous rock with a composition that is similar to granite. ....

Literacy Connection

Summarize Text Underline the sentence that best summarizes the paragraph.

Sedimentary Rock

Most **sedimentary rock** (sed uh MEN tur ee) forms when small particles of rocks or the remains of plants and animals are pressed and cemented together in the process of sedimentation. The raw material is **sediment**—small, solid pieces of material that come from rocks or living things. As shown in **Figure 4**, sediment forms and becomes sedimentary rock through a sequence of processes: weathering and erosion, transportation, deposition, compaction, and cementation. Examples of sedimentary rock include sandstone, shale, and limestone.

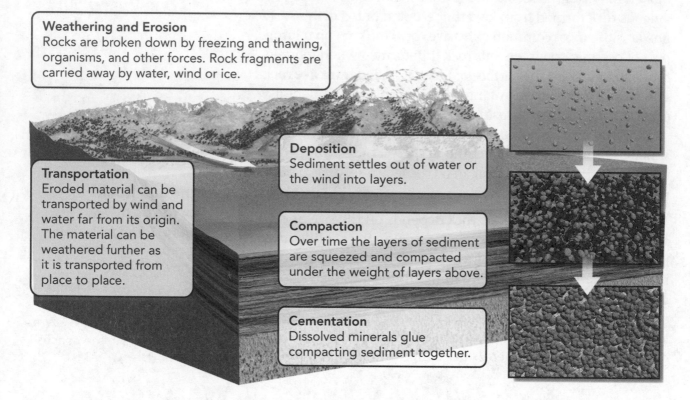

Weathering and Erosion
Rocks are broken down by freezing and thawing, organisms, and other forces. Rock fragments are carried away by water, wind or ice.

Deposition
Sediment settles out of water or the wind into layers.

Transportation
Eroded material can be transported by wind and water far from its origin. The material can be weathered further as it is transported from place to place.

Compaction
Over time the layers of sediment are squeezed and compacted under the weight of layers above.

Cementation
Dissolved minerals glue compacting sediment together.

Sequencing Sedimentary Rock Formation

Figure 4 Sedimentary rock forms in layers that are then buried below the surface. Formation occurs through a series of processes over millions of years.

1. **CCC Patterns** 🖊 Summarize how sedimentary rock forms by using the flow chart to sequence the following processes correctly: *transportation, compaction, cementation, weathering and erosion,* and *deposition.*

2. **Synthesize Information** Which two processes turn layers of loose sediment into hard sedimentary rock?

....

....

Metamorphic Rock

Metamorphic rock (met uh MOR fik) forms when a rock is changed by heat or pressure, by chemical reactions. When high heat and pressure are **applied** to rock, the rock's shape, texture, or composition can change, as shown in **Figure 5**.

Most metamorphic rock forms deep inside Earth, where both heat and pressure are much greater than at Earth's surface. Collisions between Earth's plates can push rock down toward the deeper, hotter mantle, altering the rock. The heat that changes rock into metamorphic rock can also come from very hot magma that rises up into colder rock. The high heat of this magma changes surrounding rock into metamorphic rock.

Very high pressure can also change rock into metamorphic rock. When plates collide, or when rock is buried deep beneath millions of tons of rock, the pressure can be enough to chemically change the rock's minerals to other types. The physical appearance, texture, and crystal structure of the minerals changes as a result.

Metamorphic rocks whose grains are arranged in parallel layers or bands are said to be foliated. For example, the crystals in granite can be flattened to form the foliated texture of gneiss. Some metamorphic rocks, such as marble, are nonfoliated. Their mineral grains are arranged randomly.

✅ **CHECK POINT** **Summarize Text** How is the formation of igneous rock different from metamorphic rock?

....

....

Academic Vocabulary

Applied is the past tense of the verb *apply*. What is applied to rock that causes the rock to change shape and composition? Underline your answer in the text.

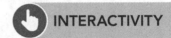 **INTERACTIVITY**

Explore different regions' rocks.

Granite

Heat and Pressure

Gneiss

Marble

Heat and Pressure

Limestone

Metamorphic Changes

Figure 5 🖉 Heat and pressure can change one type of rock into another. Label each rock *sedimentary*, *igneous*, or *metamorphic*. Indicate whether the metamorphic rocks are foliated. Then shade the correct arrowhead to show which rock can form from the other rock.

Eruption!

Figure 6 A volcanic eruption brings up magma that will be subject to weathering and erosion when it cools.

Evaluate Change Would you describe the processes that change the rocks making up this volcano as fast or slow? Explain.

....

....

....

....

The Flow of Energy No matter what type of rock is formed, it formed as a result of the energy that flows through the Earth system. The energy that drives forces affecting the formation of sedimentary rock, such as weathering, erosion, transportation, and deposition, comes in the form of heat from the sun. Heat from Earth's interior drives the processes that control the formation of igneous and metamorphic rocks.

✓ CHECK POINT **Determine Conclusions** What are the sources of energy that drive rock formation?

....

....

....

Math Toolbox

Pressure and Depth

Pressure increases inside Earth as depth increases.

1. SEP Interpret Data About how far must one travel to experience the greatest pressure inside Earth?

....

2. Analyze Relationships How is pressure related to depth?

....

....

Pressure vs. Depth Inside Earth

(Graph: Pressure (GPa) on y-axis ranging 0 to 350; Depth (km) on x-axis ranging 0 to 6,000. Curve rises from origin, increasing pressure with depth, leveling off near 350 GPa at about 6,000 km.)

1. **Identify** What are the three major kinds of rocks?

....

....

2. **CCC Cause and Effect** What is the source of energy that drives the weathering and erosion of sedimentary rock? Explain.

....

....

....

....

3. **SEP Evaluate Evidence** High heat melts a deposit of sedimentary rock, which then hardens into new rock. What kind of rock forms? Explain your answer.

....

....

....

....

....

4. **Analyze Properties** You are examining a sample of igneous rock. What factors affect the kind of igneous rock found in the sample?

....

....

....

....

....

5. **SEP Construct Explanations** If rocks, such as the sandstone formations in **Figure 1**, are constantly changing as a result of weathering and erosion, then why do they appear to be stable and unchanging to us?

....

....

....

....

....

....

....

Quest CHECK-IN

In this lesson, you learned about rocks and how energy from the sun and Earth's interior drives their formation.

SEP Use Models How could the formation of metamorphic rock be modeled in a science fiction film through special effects?

....

....

....

....

☝ INTERACTIVITY

Rocky Business

Go online to evaluate the science facts in a movie script and the ways they are presented, revising the script as necessary.

(4) Cycling of Rocks

ʍInvestigate Hypothesize about how rocks are related and how they may have formed.

MS-ESS2-1 Develop a model to describe the cycling of Earth's materials and the flow of energy that drives this process.

Connect It !

✏ **Look closely at the desert photograph in Figure 1. Circle a change that you can observe in the image.**

CCC Stability and Change What change did you observe? What agent is causing the change?

....

....

CCC Stability and Change What rock-forming processes are taking place?

....

....

The Cycling of Earth's Materials

The rock in Earth's crust is always changing. Forces deep inside Earth and at the surface build, destroy, and change the rocks in the crust. The **rock cycle** is the series of processes that occur on Earth's surface and in the crust and mantle that slowly change rocks from one kind to another. For example, the **process** of weathering breaks down granite into sediment that gets carried away and dropped by the wind. Some of that sediment can later form sandstone. The stage of the rock cycle shown in **Figure 1**, is sediment. This sediment can travel by wind and eventually form rock.

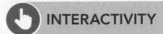

INTERACTIVITY

Explore the different phases of the rock cycle.

Academic Vocabulary

Circle the name of a process in the text. Then name two processes you go through in your daily life.

....

HANDS-ON LAB

и**Investigate** Hypothesize about how rocks are related and how they may have formed.

Rock Cycle in Action

Figure 1 In Death Valley, California, and other locations on Earth's surface, processes of the rock cycle continuously move and change sediment and rocks.

Half Dome

Figure 2 Processes in the rock cycle change the granite in Half Dome.

1. **SEP Evidence** Circle the words that best complete the sentences. The (leaves / roots) of the trees on the mountain cause (weathering / erosion) of the granite. (Erosion / Deposition) by streams transports sediment away.

2. **Reason Quantitatively** How long will it most likely take for processes in the rock cycle to change most of Half Dome into sediment? Check the box next to the correct answer.

☐ less than 1 million years
☐ 1 million years
☐ 10 million years or more

The Flow of Energy in the Rock Cycle

The pathways by which rocks move through the rock cycle are processes and events they that repeat again and again. **Figure 2** shows Half Dome located in Yosemite National Park, California. The granite in Half Dome formed millions of years ago below Earth's surface as magma cooled.

After the granite formed, the forces of mountain building slowly pushed the granite up to the surface. Since then, weathering by plants and environmental conditions and erosion have been breaking down and carrying away the granite. Some of the weathered granite, called sediment, is transported to other parts of the mountain to become soil for organisms to live in. Some is moved by streams to rivers and eventually to the ocean.

For millions of years, layers of sediment build up on the ocean floor. Slowly, the weight of the layers compacts the sediment. Then calcite dissolved in the ocean water cements the particles together, causing a chemical change in the material. Over time, the material that once formed the igneous rock granite of Half Dome could become the sedimentary rock sandstone.

Sediment could keep piling up on the sandstone. The motion of Earth's plates could move the sandstone even deeper below the surface. Extreme pressure could deform the rocks by compacting, and causing physical and chemical changes in the rock particles. Silica, the main ingredient in quartz, could replace the calcite cement. The rock's physical texture would change from gritty to smooth. After millions of years, the sandstone could change into the metamorphic rock quartzite. Or, the heat below Earth's surface could melt the sandstone and form magma, renewing the cycle. **Figure 3** shows this process.

Literacy Connection

Translate Information
Review the sequence of events described in the text. Then number the materials from Half Dome in the order in which they move through the rock cycle.

Sandstone ....

Granite ....

Quartzite ....

Sediment ....

The Rock Cycle

Figure 3 Patterns of repeating events in the rock cycle, including melting, weathering, erosion, and the application of heat and pressure, constantly change rocks from one type into another type. Through these events, Earth's materials get recycled.

INTERACTIVITY

Have an interactive look at the rock cycle.

1. **SEP Develop Models** ✏ Study the photographs of the Earth materials. Fill in each blank box in the rock cycle diagram with the correct material.

2. **SEP Use Models** ✏ Study the diagram. Then label each arrow with the correct term: *melting, weathering and erosion, heat and pressure, volcanic activity,* or *deposition.* (*Hint:* To fit your answers, abbreviate "weathering and erosion" as "w & e.")

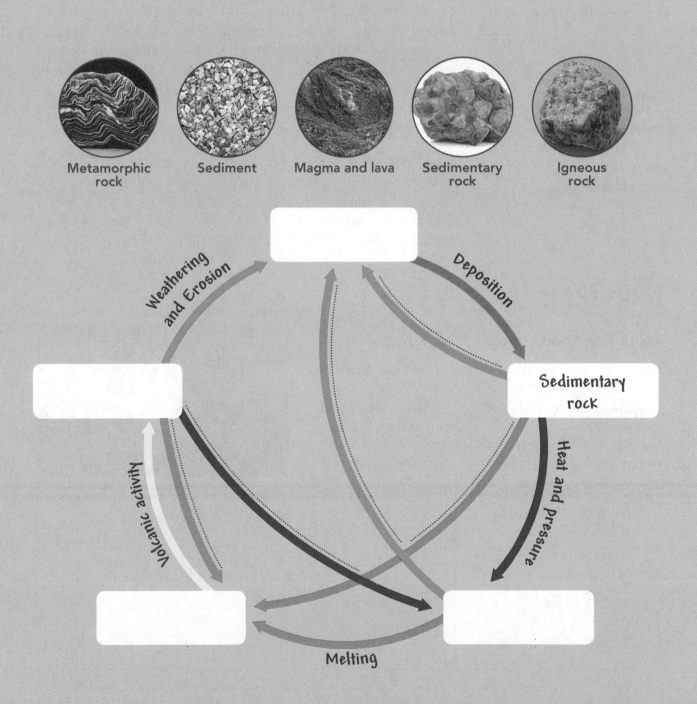

109

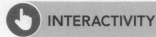

INTERACTIVITY

Track Earth materials as they move through the rock cycle.

✓ CHECK POINT

Cause and Effect Underline the plate motion that can lead to rock changing into metamorphic rock.

Plate Tectonics and the Rock Cycle

The rock cycle is driven in part by plate tectonics. The Earth's lithosphere is made up of huge plates that slowly move over Earth's surface due to convection currents in the mantle. As the plates move, they carry the continents and ocean floors with them. Plate movements help drive the rock cycle by helping to form magma, the **source** of igneous rock.

Where oceanic plates move apart, magma moves upward and fills the gap with new igneous rock. Where an oceanic plate moves beneath a continental plate, magma forms and rises. The result is a volcano where lava flows onto the overlying plate, forming igneous rock. Sedimentary rock can also result from plate movement. The collision of continental plates can be strong enough to push up a mountain range. Weathering and erosion wear away mountains and produce sediment that may eventually become sedimentary rock. Finally, a collision between continental plates can push rocks down deep beneath the surface. Here, heat and pressure could change the rocks to metamorphic rock.

Cycling of Earth's Materials

As the rock in Earth's crust moves through the rock cycle, material is not lost or gained. Instead it changes form and gets recycled. For example, basalt that forms from hardened lava can weather and erode to form sediment. The sediment can eventually form new rock.

Model It !

Modeling the Cycling of Rock Material

Figure 4 New rock forms from erupting lava where two plates move apart on the ocean floor.

SEP Develop Models ✏ Complete the diagram to model how rock material might cycle from lava to sedimentary rock. Draw and label three more possible events in this pattern of change in the rock cycle.

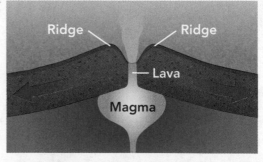

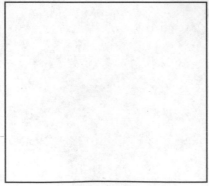

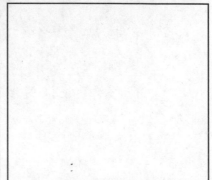

☑ LESSON 4 Check

MS-ESS2-1

1. CCC Stability and Change What processes can recycle sedimentary rock into sediment?

Weathering and erosion.

2. CCC Patterns Describe a process that happens again and again in the rock cycle.

Weathering and erosion change sedimentary rock that was formed into sediment.

3. SEP Construct Explanations Explain why the change from metamorphic rock to magma almost always occurs below Earth's surface.

This is because it needs to cool slowly with heat and pressure.

4. SEP Evaluate Evidence Do you think that plate tectonics plays a major or minor role in the rock cycle? Explain your answer.

major, they change rocks with heat and pressure.

Use the rock cycle diagram in Figure 3 to help you answer Question 5.

5. SEP Use Models Describe two different ways that sedimentary rock can become igneous rock.

Deposition
Heat and pressure
Cementing

Quest CHECK-IN

In this lesson, you learned how Earth's materials move through the rock cycle. You also learned about the flow of energy that drives the processes of the rock cycle.

SEP Ask Questions Suppose you could meet with a science consultant for movies and scripts. What questions would you have for the consultant about reviewing, evaluating, and revising scripts to make them more scientifically accurate?

👆 INTERACTIVITY

The Rock Cyclers

Go online to identify and evaluate scientific facts of the rock cycle in a movie script, and then revise the script to make it more accurate.

MS-ESS2-1

Evidence-Based Assessment

Earth's layers vary in thickness, temperature, pressure, density, state of matter, and composition. The infographic below compares some of these characteristics of Earth's layers.

Analyze the infographic to answer the questions.

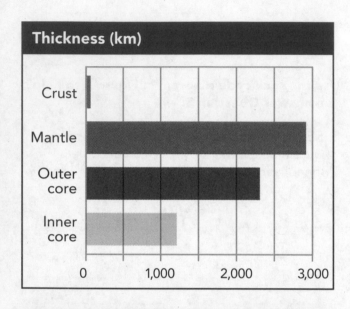

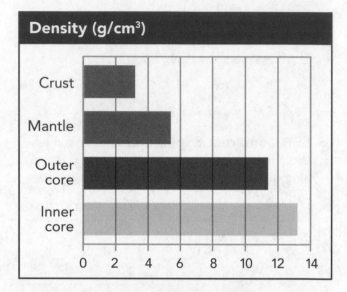

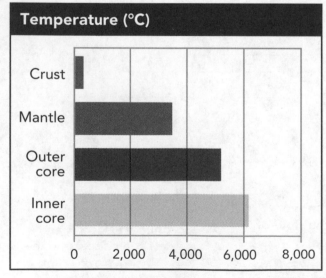

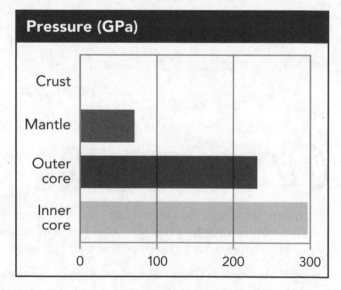

1. **SEP Analyze Data** Rank the following layers of Earth from thickest to thinnest where 1 is the thickest and 4 is the thinnest.
   A. crust ....
   B. outer core ....
   C. mantle ....
   D. inner core ....

2. **SEP Analyze Data** Approximately how many times denser is the liquid outer core than the solid crust?
   A. 2   B. 4
   C. 5   D. 7

3. **CCC Cause and Effect** Suppose the mantle were thicker than it is. What effect would this have on the pressure in the outer core? Explain.

   ....
   ....
   ....
   ....
   ....

4. **CCC Patterns** Circle the words that correctly describe the relationship among density, pressure, and temperature in Earth's layers.

   From the crust down through the inner core, density, pressure, and temperature all (increase / decrease). The bottom-most layer will be (hotter / cooler) and (denser / less dense) because of an (increase / decrease) in pressure.

5. **Synthesize Information** Describe how some of the characteristics of the mantle contribute to the cycling of materials and energy flow on Earth.

   ....
   ....
   ....
   ....
   ....
   ....
   ....
   ....

Quest FINDINGS

Complete the Quest!

Review and revise the movie scripts. Consider how you can stage readings of the scripts.

Defend Your Claim Do you think producers of fictional films that depict scientific processes should be required to hire a science consultant? Support your opinion with facts and details.

....
....
....
....
....
....

INTERACTIVITY

Reflect on Science in the Movies

MS-ESS2-1

The Rock Cycle in Action

Can you make **models** that show **third-grade students** how sedimentary, igneous, and metamorphic **rocks** form?

Background

Phenomenon At first glance, rock formations—such as the Vasquez Rocks in California shown here—don't seem to do much other than sit motionless. But rocks are constantly being cycled through processes that can take just a few minutes or thousands of years.

Your task is to work with a partner to design and build models that could be used to show how the rock cycle works to someone who has never heard of it. Your teacher will assign you a specific type of rock—sedimentary, metamorphic, or igneous—and you will design a model of its formation.

Materials

(per group)

- crayons or crayon rocks of a few different colors
- plastic knife
- paper plates
- aluminum foil
- books or other heavy objects
- hot water or hot plate
- tongs or oven mitts
- beaker

Safety

Be sure to follow all safety guidelines provided by your teacher. Appendix A of your textbook provides more details about the safety icons.

Plan Your Investigation

☐ You will create a plan and design a procedure to model the processes that form the type of rock that has been assigned to you. You must consider:

- the roles that weathering and erosion, deposition, and cementation play in forming sedimentary rock
- the role that high amounts of pressure and energy play in forming metamorphic rock
- the role that high amounts of heat and energy play in forming igneous rock

HANDS-ON LAB

ⁱⁱ**Demonstrate** Go online for a downloadable worksheet for this lab.

☐ As you design your model, consider these questions:

- What will the different crayons represent in your model?
- How can you use the available materials to represent specific processes such as weathering and erosion, or melting and cementation?
- How can you use the available materials to simulate the processes and flow of energy, such as heat and pressure, that result in the formation of sedimentary, metamorphic, and igneous rocks?

☐ Organize your ideas in the table. Then plan your procedure.

Processes	Materials	Notes
1. Weathering and erosion to form sediment		
2. Formation of sedimentary rock		
3. Formation of metamorphic rock		
4. Formation of igneous rock		

uDemonstrate Lab

Procedure

Use the space below to describe your model(s) and list steps in a procedure to demonstrate the formation of your assigned rock type. You may wish to use sketches to show some steps.

Analyze and Interpret Data

1. **SEP Develop Models** Work with other pairs to develop a complete model of the rock cycle. Draw your model in the space provided. Include labels to explain what each part of the model represents.

2. **Relate Change** Describe the flow of energy and cycling of matter represented by your pair's model. How does your model help you to understand processes that can last thousands of years?

....

....

....

....

3. **Identify Limitations** How does your model differ from the actual rock cycle on Earth? How could you make your model more accurate?

....

....

....

....

....

....

MS-ESS2-1, EP&CIIIa

Mighty Mauna Loa

The high summit of Mauna Loa is often surrounded by tropical rain clouds. The large volcano, outlined in red on the satellite image below, makes up a majority of the area of the main island of Hawaii.

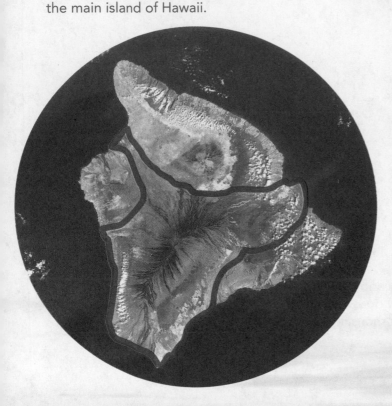

Mauna Loa is one of Hawaii's most active volcanoes, located on the largest of the islands. The volcano sits on an active hotspot. For more than 80 million years, the Hawaiian Islands and seamounts have formed as the Pacific Plate has been sliding northwest over a hotspot—a plume of magma that causes eruptions through the overlying plate.

Mauna Loa illustrates the rock cycle in action. Over time, rock will continue to be buried as more lava flows and more sediment is carried down the volcano. Under high temperatures and pressure, some of the sedimentary rock will become metamorphic rock.

When Mauna Loa erupts, magma from inside Earth pours out of the volcano as lava. The lava flows down the slopes of the volcano.

Lava cools to form igneous rock. Some lava slowly cools on the slopes of the volcano. Other lava flows to the ocean, where the lava quickly cools and increases the size of the island over time.

Weathering and erosion break down some of the igneous rock. Through the process of deposition, some of this sediment is carried down the volcano. As the sediment becomes compacted, it forms sedimentary rock.

1. **SEP Develop Models** ✏ Complete the diagram using arrows, labels, and captions to describe the processes that drive the rock cycle on Mauna Loa.

2. **CCC Patterns** The last few eruptions of Mauna Loa happened in 1942, 1949, 1950, 1975, and 1984. The volcano has erupted 33 times since 1843. When do you think the next eruption will occur, and why do you think so?

....

....

....

....

....

....

3. **SEP Construct Explanations** Why do you think Mauna Loa erupts periodically instead of steadily?

....

....

....

....

....

Take Notes

Use this space for recording notes and sketching out ideas.

Conduct an Investigation

Evidence Now that you have learned about chemical reactions, cell processes, and rocks and minerals, complete the following tasks.

Assess Impacts of Acidification

Ocean acidification impacts shallow, coastal waters much more than deeper waters. As a result, all organisms living in the waters surrounding the Channel Islands are affected. Some organisms are more vulnerable than others. Some organisms are impacted directly, and some indirectly.

When the level of acidity in ocean water increases, the amount of available calcium carbonate minerals decreases. These minerals are necessary for living things to grow bones and shells. Any organism with a skeleton, shell, or hearing organ made of calcium compounds will suffer the harmful effects of acidification, such as damaged shells, thinner shells, slowed growth, decreased egg hatching, or death.

Not all of California's coastal waters are increasing in acidity. Factors such as location, depth, the strength of currents, and water temperature all play a role. Scientists have found regions where the water is less acidic. These areas are safe havens that shelter many marine organisms.

Certain species might benefit from increased carbon dioxide in the water. Think about what you learned about cell processes. One group of living things needs carbon dioxide to grow and produce food.

NOAA scientists research the effects of ocean acidification. The data they collect will help them predict what happens as carbon dioxide levels rise.

Communicate Collaboratively With a partner, predict the likely effect of increased levels of carbon dioxide on each organism in the table. Conduct research to find additional information you might need from print and online sources. Be sure to use effective search terms and to evaluate the credibility and accuracy of each source you find. Discuss the reasoning behind your predictions.

Ocean Organisms around the Channel Islands	
Organism	**Description**
Palm Kelp *Pterygophora californica*	Brown seaweed grows to 3 m in height. Photosynthetic. Clings to rocks. Commonly dies after being torn from rocks during storms.
Moonglow Anemone *Anthopleura artemisia*	Soft, colorful animal related to jellyfish. Young are zooplankton. Adults buried partly in sand. Many stinging tentacles catch plankton drifting past.
Bat Star *Patiria miniata*	Brightly colored starfish with 5–9 arms. Internal skeleton of calcium carbonate. Eats living or dead organisms on the sea floor.
Black and Yellow Rockfish *Sebastes chrysomelas*	Bony fish with skeleton containing calcium compounds. Young rockfish are zooplankton. Older fish live in the kelp forest and eat zooplankton.
Sea Lion *Zalophus californianus*	Mammal with calcium-containing bones. Eats squid, fish, and clams. Commonly eaten by killer whales and large sharks.
Diatoms *Vaucheria* and others	Algae forming a fuzzy layer on underwater rocks or floating in water. Photosynthetic. The most common type of phytoplankton.
Eelgrass *Zostera marina*	Flowering plant preferring sheltered, sandy seafloor. Provides shelter for many young animals. Major source of food for seabirds, crabs, and shrimp.
Orange Puffball Sponge *Tethya californiana*	Ball-shaped sponge living in the kelp forest. Simple animal with calcium-containing skeleton. Filters particles of food from water. Young are zooplankton.
Ornate Tube Worm *Diopatra ornata*	Seafloor worm lives in a protective tube of chitin, the material of insect shells. Tube is decorated with shells and bits of stone. Tube worms filter plankton from water for food. Young tube worms are zooplankton.
Barnacle *Megabalanus californicus*	Brightly-colored shellfish attached to rocks. Shell is calcium carbonate. Feathery legs filter plankton from the water to eat. Young barnacles are zooplankton.

Based on you and your partner's predictions, answer the following questions.

1. **SEP Construct Explanations** Which of the listed species are most likely to be harmed by increased ocean acidification? What makes them vulnerable?

   Bat Star, Rockfish, Sea Lion, Puffball Sponge, Barnacle They all contain some form of calcium.

2. **Explain Phenomena** Which species are most likely to be helped by increased ocean acidification? Why?

   Palm kelp, Anemone, Diatoms, eelgrass, Tubeworm. The food will be already broken down for them.

3. **SEP Engage in Argument** Do you think there is a level of acidification that is harmful to every species? Explain your reasoning.

   Yes. I think this because if PH levels go too high, it can burn everything.

4. **CCC Stability and Change** Scientists need more data about the effects of ocean acidification. Only a few research projects have been done in the deep waters of the open ocean. More data will help them make the best decisions for managing wildlife and natural areas. What do you think could help fill the holes in the scientific knowledge about ocean acidification and the Channel Islands? Describe a potential research project.

   They could check all animals in the area, and see how the population changes, and how the animals and plants are affected.

Safety Symbols

These symbols warn of possible dangers in the laboratory and remind you to work carefully.

 Safety Goggles Wear safety goggles to protect your eyes in any activity involving chemicals, flames or heating, or glassware.

 Lab Apron Wear a laboratory apron to protect your skin and clothing from damage.

 Breakage Handle breakable materials, such as glassware, with care. Do not touch broken glassware.

 Heat-Resistant Gloves Use an oven mitt or other hand protection when handling hot materials, such as hot plates or hot glassware.

 Plastic Gloves Wear disposable plastic gloves when working with harmful chemicals and organisms. Keep your hands away from your face, and dispose of the gloves according to your teacher's instructions.

 Heating Use a clamp or tongs to pick up hot glassware. Do not touch hot objects with your bare hands.

 Flames Before you work with flames, tie back loose hair and clothing. Follow your teacher's instructions about lighting and extinguishing flames.

 No Flames When using flammable materials, make sure there are no flames, sparks, or other exposed heat sources present.

 Corrosive Chemical Avoid getting acid or other corrosive chemicals on your skin or clothing or in your eyes. Do not inhale the vapors. Wash your hands after the activity.

 Poison Do not let any poisonous chemical come into contact with your skin, and do not inhale its vapors. Wash your hands when you are finished with the activity.

 Fumes Work in a well-ventilated area when harmful vapors may be involved. Avoid inhaling vapors directly. Test an odor only when directed to do so by your teacher, and use a wafting motion to direct the vapor toward your nose.

 Sharp Object Scissors, scalpels, knives, needles, pins, and tacks can cut your skin. Always direct a sharp edge or point away from yourself and others.

 Animal Safety Treat live or preserved animals or animal parts with care to avoid harming the animals or yourself. Wash your hands when you are finished with the activity.

 Plant Safety Handle plants only as directed by your teacher. If you are allergic to certain plants, tell your teacher; do not do an activity involving those plants. Avoid touching harmful plants such as poison ivy. Wash your hands when you are finished with the activity.

 Electric Shock To avoid electric shock, never use electrical equipment around water, when the equipment is wet, or when your hands are wet. Be sure cords are untangled and cannot trip anyone. Unplug equipment not in use.

 Physical Safety When an experiment involves physical activity, avoid injuring yourself or others. Alert your teacher if there is any reason you should not participate.

 Disposal Dispose of chemicals and other laboratory materials safely. Follow the instructions from your teacher.

 Hand Washing Wash your hands thoroughly when finished with an activity. Use soap and warm water. Rinse well.

 General Safety Awareness When this symbol appears, follow the instructions provided. When you are asked to develop your own procedure in a lab, have your teacher approve your plan.

APPENDIX B

Periodic Table of Elements

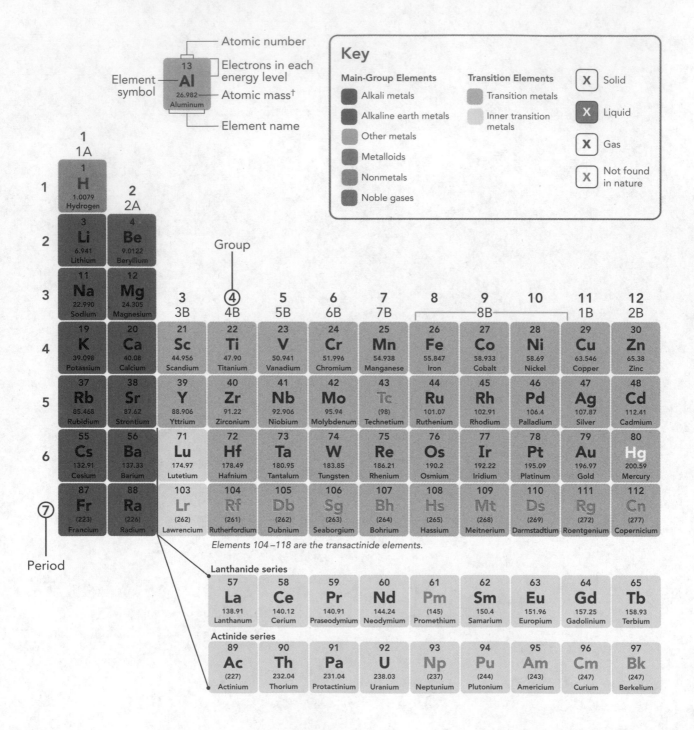

Atomic number

Electrons in each energy level

Element symbol — **Al** 26.982 Aluminum — Atomic mass†

Element name

Key

Main-Group Elements
- Alkali metals
- Alkaline earth metals
- Other metals
- Metalloids
- Nonmetals
- Noble gases

Transition Elements
- Transition metals
- Inner transition metals

- X Solid
- X Liquid
- X Gas
- X Not found in nature

Elements 104–118 are the transactinide elements.

Lanthanide series

| 57 La 138.91 Lanthanum | 58 Ce 140.12 Cerium | 59 Pr 140.91 Praseodymium | 60 Nd 144.24 Neodymium | 61 Pm (145) Promethium | 62 Sm 150.4 Samarium | 63 Eu 151.96 Europium | 64 Gd 157.25 Gadolinium | 65 Tb 158.93 Terbium |

Actinide series

| 89 Ac (227) Actinium | 90 Th 232.04 Thorium | 91 Pa 231.04 Protactinium | 92 U 238.03 Uranium | 93 Np (237) Neptunium | 94 Pu (244) Plutonium | 95 Am (243) Americium | 96 Cm (247) Curium | 97 Bk (247) Berkelium |

†The atomic masses in parentheses are the mass numbers of the longest-lived isotope of elements for which a standard atomic mass cannot be defined.

13 3A	14 4A	15 5A	16 6A	17 7A	18 8A
					2 **He** 4.0026 Helium
5 **B** 10.81 Boron	6 **C** 12.011 Carbon	7 **N** 14.007 Nitrogen	8 **O** 15.999 Oxygen	9 **F** 18.998 Fluorine	10 **Ne** 20.179 Neon
13 **Al** 26.982 Aluminum	14 **Si** 28.086 Silicon	15 **P** 30.974 Phosphorus	16 **S** 32.06 Sulfur	17 **Cl** 35.453 Chlorine	18 **Ar** 39.948 Argon
31 **Ga** 69.72 Gallium	32 **Ge** 72.59 Germanium	33 **As** 74.922 Arsenic	34 **Se** 78.96 Selenium	35 **Br** 79.904 Bromine	36 **Kr** 83.80 Krypton
49 **In** 114.82 Indium	50 **Sn** 118.69 Tin	51 **Sb** 121.75 Antimony	52 **Te** 127.60 Tellurium	53 **I** 126.90 Iodine	54 **Xe** 131.30 Xenon
81 **Tl** 204.37 Thallium	82 **Pb** 207.2 Lead	83 **Bi** 208.98 Bismuth	84 **Po** (209) Polonium	85 **At** (210) Astatine	86 **Rn** (222) Radon
113 **Nh** (284) Nihonium	114 **Fl** (289) Flerovium	115 **Mc** (288) Moscovium	116 **Lv** (292) Livermorium	117 **Ts** (294) Tennessine	118 **Og** (294) Oganesson

66 **Dy** 162.50 Dysprosium	67 **Ho** 164.93 Holmium	68 **Er** 167.26 Erbium	69 **Tm** 168.93 Thulium	70 **Yb** 173.04 Ytterbium
98 **Cf** (251) Californium	99 **Es** (252) Einsteinium	100 **Fm** (257) Fermium	101 **Md** (258) Mendelevium	102 **No** (259) Nobelium

GLOSSARY

A

abiotic factor A nonliving part of an organism's habitat.

alluvial fan A wide, sloping deposit of sediment formed where a stream leaves a mountain range.

autotroph An organism that is able to capture energy from sunlight or chemicals and use it to produce its own food.

atom The basic unit from which all matter is made.

B

biodiversity The number and variety of different species in an area.

biotic factor A living or once living part of an organism's habitat.

boiling point The temperature at which a liquid boils.

C

cellular respiration The process in which oxygen and glucose undergo a complex series of chemical reactions inside cells, releasing energy.

chemical change A change in which one or more substances combine or break apart to form new substances.

chemical property A characteristic of a substance that describes its ability to change into different substances.

chemical weathering The process that breaks down rock through chemical changes.

chlorophyll A green photosynthetic pigment found in the chloroplasts of plants, algae, and some bacteria.

closed system A system in which no matter is allowed to enter or leave.

commensalism A type of symbiosis between two species in which one species benefits and the other species is neither helped nor harmed.

community All the different populations that live together in a certain area.

competition The struggle between organisms to survive as they attempt to use the same limited resources in the same place at the same time.

compound A substance made of two or more elements chemically combined in a specific ratio, or proportion.

compression Stress that squeezes rock until it folds or breaks.

condensation The change in state from a gas to a liquid.

conservation The practice of using less of a resource so that it can last longer.

consumer An organism that obtains energy by feeding on other organisms.

continental glacier A glacier that covers much of a continent or large island.

convergent boundary A plate boundary where two plates move toward each other.

crust The layer of rock that forms Earth's outer surface.

crystal A solid in which the atoms are arranged in a pattern that repeats again and again.

crystallization The process by which atoms are arranged to form a material with a crystal structure.

crystallize To form a crystal structure.

D

decomposer An organism that gets energy by breaking down biotic wastes and dead organisms and returns raw materials to the soil and water.

deflation The process by which wind removes surface materials.

delta A landform made of sediment that is deposited where a river flows into an ocean or lake.

density The measurement of how much mass of a substance is contained in a given volume.

deposition Process in which sediment is laid down in new locations.

desalination A process that removes salt from sea water to make fresh water.

divergent boundary A plate boundary where two plates move away from each other.

dormant Term used to describe a volcano that is not currently acrtive but able to become active in the future.

drought A long period of low precipitation.

E

earthquake The shaking that results from the movement of rock beneath Earth's surface.

ecological restoration The practice of helping a degraded or destroyed ecosystem recover from damage.

ecology The study of how organisms interact with each other and their environment.

ecosystem The community of organisms that live in a particular area, along with their nonliving environment.

ecosystem services The benefits that humans derive from ecosystems.

element A pure substance that cannot be broken down into other substances by chemical or physical means.

energy pyramid A diagram that shows the amount of energy that moves from one feeding level to another in a food web.

erosion The process by which water, ice, wind, or gravity moves weathered particles of rock and soil.

evaporation The process by which molecules at the surface of a liquid absorb enough energy to change to a gas.

extinct volcano Term used to describe a volcano that is no longer active and unlikely to erupt again

extinction The disappearance of all members of a species from Earth.

F

fault A break in Earth's crust along which rocks move.

fermentation The process by which cells release energy by breaking down food molecules without using oxygen.

flood An overflowing of water in a normally dry area.

flood plain The flat, wide area of land along a river.

food chain A series of events in an ecosystem in which organisms transfer energy by eating and by being eaten.

food web The pattern of overlapping feeding relationships or food chains among the various organisms in an ecosystem.

fossil fuel Energy-rich substance formed from the remains of organisms.

freezing point The temperature at which a liquid freezes.

G

gas A state of matter with no definite shape or volume.

glacier Any large mass of ice that moves slowly over land.

groundwater Water that fills the cracks and spaces in underground soil and rock layers.

H

habitat An environment that provides the things a specific organism needs to live, grow, and reproduce.

heterotroph An organism that cannot make its own food and gets food by consuming other living things.

hot spot An area where magma from deep within the mantle melts through the crust above it.

humus Dark-colored organic material in soil.

hurricane A tropical storm that has winds of about 119 kilometers per hour or higher.

I

ice age Time in Earth's history during which glaciers covered large parts of the surface.

igneous rock A type of rock that forms from the cooling of molten rock at or below the surface.

inner core A dense sphere of solid iron and nickel at the center of Earth.

GLOSSARY

invasive species Species that are not native to a habitat and can out-compete native species in an ecosystem.

K

keystone species A species that influences the survival of many other species in an ecosystem.

L

lava Liquid magma that reaches the surface.

limiting factor An environmental factor that causes a population to decrease in size.

liquid A state of matter that has no definite shape but has a definite volume.

loess A wind-formed deposit made of fine particles of clay and silt.

longshore drift The movement of water and sediment down a beach caused by waves coming in to shore at an angle.

M

magma A molten mixture of rock-forming substances, gases, and water from the mantle.

magnitude The measurement of an earthquake's strength based on seismic waves and movement along faults.

mantle The layer of hot, solid material between Earth's crust and core.

mass A measure of how much matter is in an object.

mass movement Any one of several processes by which gravity moves sediment downhill.

matter Anything that has mass and takes up space.

mechanical weathering The type of weathering in which rock is physically broken into smaller pieces.

melting point The temperature at which a substance changes from a solid to a liquid; the same as the freezing point, or temperature at which a liquid changes to a solid.

metamorphic rock A type of rock that forms from an existing rock that is changed by heat, pressure, or chemical reactions.

mid-ocean ridge An undersea mountain chain where new ocean floor is produced; a divergent plate boundary under the ocean.

mineral A naturally occurring solid that can form by inorganic processes and that has a crystal structure and a definite chemical composition.

mixture Two or more substances that are together in the same place, but their atoms are not chemically bonded.

molecule A group of two or more atoms held together by chemical bonds.

mutualism A type of symbiosis in which both species benefit from living together.

N

natural resource Anything naturally occurring in the environment that humans use.

nonrenewable resource A natural resource that is not replaced in a useful time frame.

nuclear fission The splitting of an atom's nucleus into two nuclei, which releases a great deal of energy.

O

ocean trench An undersea valley that represents one of the deepest parts of the ocean.

open system A system in which matter can enter from or escape to the surroundings.

ore A mineral deposit large enough and valuable enough for it to be extracted from the ground.

organism A living thing.

outer core A layer of molten iron and nickel that surrounds the inner core of Earth.

P

parasitism A type of symbiosis in which one organism lives with, on, or in a host and harms it.

petroleum Liquid fossil fuel; oil.

photosynthesis The process by which plants and other autotrophs capture and use light energy to make food from carbon dioxide and water.

physical change A change that alters the form or appearance of a material but does not make the material into another substance.

physical property A characteristic of a pure substance that can be observed without changing it into another substance.

pioneer species The first species to populate an area during succession.

plucking The process by which a glacier picks up rocks as it flows over the land.

polymer A long chain of molecules made up of repeating units.

population All the members of one species living in the same area.

precipitation Any form of water that falls from clouds and reaches Earth's surface as rain, snow, sleet, or hail.

predation An interaction in which one organism kills another for food or nutrients.

producer An organism that can make its own food.

product A substance formed as a result of a chemical reaction.

— **R** —

reactant A substance that enters into a chemical reaction.

rock cycle A series of processes on the surface and inside Earth that slowly changes rocks from one kind to another.

runoff Water that flows over the ground surface rather than soaking into the ground.

— **S** —

sand dune A deposit of wind-blown sand.

sea-floor spreading The process by which molten material adds new oceanic crust to the ocean floor.

sediment Small, solid pieces of material that come from rocks or the remains of organisms; earth materials deposited by erosion.

sedimentary rock A type of rock that forms when particles from other rocks or the remains of plants and animals are pressed and cemented together.

seismic wave Vibrations that travel through Earth carrying the energy released during an earthquake.

shearing Stress that pushes masses of rock in opposite directions, in a sideways movement.

soil The loose, weathered material on Earth's surface in which plants can grow.

solid A state of matter that has a definite shape and a definite volume.

solubility A measure of how much a substance dissolves in another substance.

storm A violent disturbance in the atmosphere.

storm surge A "dome" of water that sweeps across the coast where a hurricane lands.

stream A channel through which water is continually flowing downhill.

stress A force that acts on rock to change its shape or volume.

subduction The process by which oceanic crust sinks beneath a deep-ocean trench and back into the mantle at a convergent plate boundary.

sublimation The change in state from a solid directly to a gas without passing through the liquid state.

substance A single kind of matter that is pure and has a specific set of properties.

succession The series of predictable changes that occur in a community over time.

sustainability The ability of an ecosystem to maintain bioviersity and production indefinitely.

symbiosis Any relationship in which two species live closely together and that benefits at least one of the species.

synthetic Created or manufactured by humans; not found occurring in nature

— **T** —

temperature How hot or cold something is; a measure of the average energy of motion of the particles of a substance; the measure of the average kinetic energy of the particles of a substance.

GLOSSARY

tension Stress that stretches rock so that it becomes thinner in the middle.

thermal energy The total kinetic and potential energy of all the particles of an object.

thunderstorm A small storm often accompanied by heavy precipitation and frequent thunder and lightning.

till The sediments deposited directly by a glacier.

tornado A rapidly whirling, funnel-shaped cloud that reaches down to touch Earth's surface.

transform boundary A plate boundary where two plates move past each other in opposite directions.

tributary A stream or river that flows into a larger river.

tsunami A giant wave usually caused by an earthquake beneath the ocean floor.

U

uniformitarianism The geologic principle that the same geologic processes that operate today operated in the past to change Earth's surface.

V

valley glacier A long, narrow glacier that forms when snow and ice build up in a mountain valley.

vaporization The change of state from a liquid to a gas.

volcano A weak spot in the crust where magma has come to the surface.

volume The amount of space that matter occupies.

W

weight A measure of the force of gravity acting on an object.

INDEX

Page number in **Bold** are vocabulary terms. *Italic* page numbers are of charts, graphs, pictures, and features.

INDEX

Page number in **Bold** are vocabulary terms. *Italic* page numbers are of charts, graphs, pictures, and features.

INDEX

Page number in **Bold** are vocabulary terms. *Italic* page numbers are of charts, graphs, pictures, and features.

V

Verne, Jules, *75*
Vocabulary, Academic, 32, 54, 60, 77, 80, 92, 103, 107, 110
Volcanos, rock cycle and, *104,* 109, *118–119*

W

Water resources, purification, *29*
Waves, seismic, 78
Weathering
  rock cycle and, 107–108, 109
  of sedimentary rock, 102, 104

Writing Skills
  informative texts, 85
  summarize texts, 50, 102
  Write About It, 17, 36, 85
  See also **Science Notebook**

X

Xenoliths, *77*

Z

Zooplankton, *5*

CREDITS

Photography
Photo locators denoted as follows: Top (T), Center (C), Bottom (B), Left (L), Right (R), Background (Bkgd)

Covers
Front: Casey Kiernan/Moment/Getty Images; Meganopierson/Shutterstock; Zoonar GmbH/Alamy Stock Photo; Stocktrek Images, Inc./Alamy Stock Photo; Back: Marinello/DigitalVision Vectors/Getty Images

Instructional Segment 2
iv: Nick Lundgren/Shutterstock; vi: Frederic J. Brown/AFP/Getty Images; vii: Grobler du Preez/Shutterstock; viii: Demerzel21/Fotolia; x: Fabriziobalconi/Fotolia; x: Brian J. Skerry/National Geographic/Getty Images; xi: Dale Kolke/ZUMA Press/Newscom; 000: George H.H. Huey/Alamy Stock Photo; 002: George H.H. Huey/Alamy Stock Photo; 004CR: Kevin Schafer/Alamy Stock Photo; 004BL: Russ Bishop/Alamy Stock Photo; 004BR: Douglas Klug/Getty Images; 005CL: Douglas Klug/Getty Images; 005CR: M. I. Walker/Science Source; 005BL: FLPA/Alamy Stock Photo; 006BC: Courtesy of Nina Bednarsek; 006BL: Alexander Semenov/Science Source; 006BR: Courtesy of Nina Bednarsek; 008: Frederic J. Brown/AFP/Getty Images; 010: Steve Hix/Getty Images; 012: Vincent Grebenicek/Shutterstock; 018TC: Charles D. Winters/Science Source; 018TR: Serezniy/123RF; 021BL: John Lund/The Image Bank/Getty Images; 021BR: Interfoto/Hermann Historica/AKG Images; 022: Anastasios71/Shutterstock; 025: Chepko Danil Vitalevich/Shutterstock; 027BC: Patrick Moynihan/pyronious/Getty Images; 027BR: Evan Sharboneau/Fotolia; 029: Jake Lyell/Alamy Stock Photo; 030: Vidady/Fotolia; 031R: Feng Yu/Alamy Stock Photo; 031CL: Thewet/Fotolia; 031BCR: Penchan Gamjai/Fotolia; 033BC: Thomas J. Peterson/Alamy Stock Photo; 033TL: Naretev/Fotolia; 033CL: Shyripa Alexandr/Shutterstock; 034BL: Mau Horng/Shutterstock; 034L: Monticello/Shutterstock; 035TL: Borodin Denis/Shutterstock; 035BR: Nils Z/Shutterstock; 036BL: Oscar Dominguez/Alamy Stock Photo; 036BR: Nigel Wilkins/Alamy Stock Photo; 040: Jordeangjelovik/Shutterstock; 041: Charles D. Winters/Science Source; 044: Grobler du Preez/Shutterstock; 046Bkgd: Douglas Orton/Blend Images/Alamy Stock Photo; 046TR: Studio2013/Fotolia; 048: Andrey Nekrasov/Image Quest Marine; 049: David Courtenay/Getty Images; 050Bkgd: Shutterstock; 050T: Charlie Summers/Nature Picture Library; 050C: ArtTDi/Shutterstock; 050B: Leena Robinson/Alamy Stock Photo; 051: Tunde Gaspar/Shutterstock; 055: Sacramento Bee/ Florence Low ZUMA Press, Inc./Alamy Stock Photo; 057: Patrick T. Fallon/Bloomberg/Getty Images ; 058: Michael Reusse/Getty Images; 059: Melinda Fawver/Shutterstock; 063TL: Ramon Espelt/AGE Fotostock; 063CL: Ramon Espelt/AGE Fotostock; 063BL: Ramon Espelt/AGE Fotostock; 065Bkgd: Elena Schweitzer/Shutterstock; 065BR: M. Unal Ozmen/Shutterstock; 068: Anne Ackermann/Getty Images; 069CR: Chris Mattison/FLPA/Science Source; 069BR: Martin Shields/Alamy Stock Photo; 072: Demerzel21/Fotolia; 074: John Bryson/The LIFE Images Collection/Getty Images; 076: Wead/Shutterstock; 077: John Cancalosi/Getty Images; 087: AOES Medialab/ESA; 088: Carsten Peter/Speleoresearch & Films/Getty Images; 090: DEA/A.RIZZI/Getty Images; 094: Paul Silverman/Fundamental Photographs; 095: General Photographic Agency/Getty Images; 097TR: Eric Baccega/AGE Fotostock/Alamy Stock Photo; 097B: Per-Anders Pettersson/Getty Images; 106: Michael Routh/Alamy Stock Photo; 108: Oscity/Shutterstock; 114: Jon Bilous/Shutterstock; 115TR: I-m-a-g-e/Shutterstock; 115CR: Pavlo Burdyak/123RF; 115B: MM Studio/Fotolia; 121: NOAA.

Take Notes

Use this space for recording notes and sketching out ideas.

Use this space for recording notes and sketching out ideas.

Take Notes

Use this space for recording notes and sketching out ideas.

Take Notes